TWELVE HONG KON

In the y
will enjoy these walks.

David Eassraff
June 1984.

Twelve Hong Kong Walks

Derek Kemp

HONG KONG   OXFORD
OXFORD UNIVERSITY PRESS
1985

Oxford University Press

Oxford   New York   Toronto
Kuala Lumpur   Singapore   Hong Kong   Tokyo
Delhi   Bombay   Calcutta   Madras   Karachi
Nairobi   Dar es Salaam   Cape Town
Melbourne   Auckland

and associated companies in
Beirut   Berlin   Ibadan   Nicosia

First published by Oxford University Press by
arrangement with Gulliver Books Ltd 1985

ISBN 0 19 583737 1

OXFORD is a trade mark of Oxford University Press

Printed in Hong Kong by Golden Cup Printing Co. Ltd.
Published by Oxford University Press, Warwick House, Hong Kong

Foreword

D erek Kemp's book provides a useful guide to twelve walks in the territory and at the same time offers the interested layman a wealth of botanical information about Hong Kong's vegetation that is unavailable elsewhere.

The Hong Kong Government has very wisely set aside large areas of the territory as country parks and there is a growing interest among Hong Kong people both young and old in hiking through some of our magnificent scenery. A number of books have appeared on the market describing walks but in the present volume Dr. Kemp has successfully combined details of the walk with a most useful and interesting commentary on the plants found on each walk. As well as giving an accurate botanical description and details of the plants' biology, such as flowering time, forms of the fruit, and usefulness of the plant to man, he has also included drawings, paintings and photographs to aid in their identification.

The layman should not be discouraged by the use of botanical 'jargon'. A book of this nature necessitates the use of terminology that may seem, at first, bewildering but sensibly Dr. Kemp has appended a glossary to explain such terms as well as a series of diagrams to illustrate the salient features of flowering plants.

Once the scientific terminology has been grasped the reader may then consult more advanced textbooks to widen his knowledge of particular plants or groups of plants. With this aspect in mind the author has appended a bibliography of useful reference works.

I unreservedly recommend this book and I would urge anyone who has an interest in our countryside to Walk, Observe and Learn; *Twelve Hong Kong Walks* admirably equips the interested person for this endeavour.

D.A. Griffiths
Professor of Botany
Hong Kong University

Contents

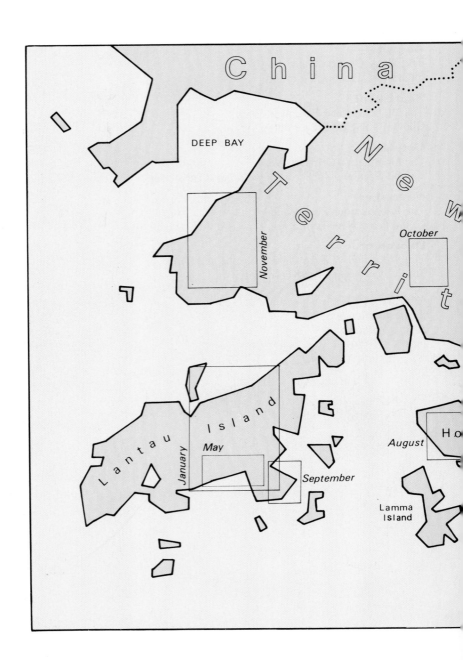

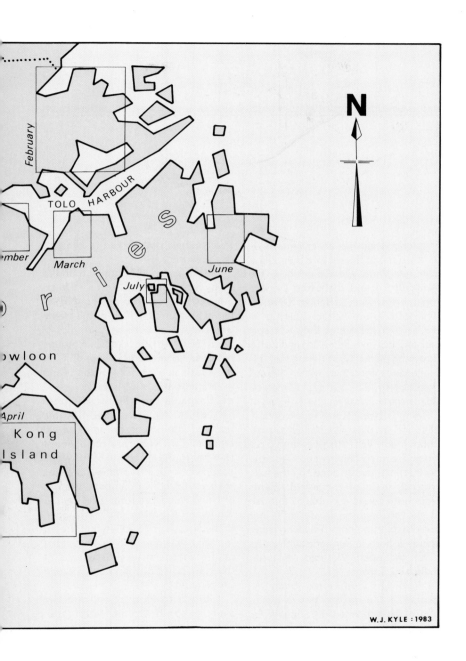

February

TOLO HARBOUR

S

e

mber

March

i

June

July

r

)

wloon

April

Kong
Island

N

Introduction

Consider the lilies of the field, how they grow; they toil
not, neither do they spin:
And yet I say unto you, even Solomon in all his glory
was not arrayed like one of these.

Matthew 6: 28—9

Hong Kong has an enormous diversity of flora. More than 2,502 vascular plants are recorded by the Agriculture and Fisheries Department as growing in Hong Kong, of which 1,875 are native. This list includes 175 species of ferns, 31 species of pines and their allies and 2,296 flowering plants. Considering that this plant life is contained within a small area of just 1,052 square kilometres, this is remarkable.

Why is Hong Kong so exceptionally rich in plant life? The answer undoubtedly lies in its geographic position. Located half-way between the northern temperate zone and the fully tropical areas of the world, plants from both zones are able to flourish in the hospitable climate. It is not surprising, therefore, that Hong Kong shares a flora in common with parts of China, Japan, Vietnam, Malaysia, India and Taiwan.

Asia has commonly been regarded as the melting pot of evolution of both plants and animals. Its vast land mass, plus a climate varying from arctic to fully tropical, has produced an amazing diversity of species that have spread to all parts of the world.

Rare species may still be found in Hong Kong and south-eastern China. Among the rare trees growing in Hong Kong are the King of the Hanging Bells *(Rhodoleia championi)*, which bears attractive bell-like groups of cerise flowers and occurs only on the south side of Hong Kong Island in limited patches of woodland, and the Foxglove Tree *(Paulownia fortunei)*, which has a scattered distribution and appears on the brink of extinction. Two very rare members of the Magnolia Family — *Michelia maudiae* and *Manglietia fordiana* —are found in the mountainous areas of Hong Kong, the former on Lantau island and the latter at Tai Mo Shan in the New Territories. In fact the *M. fordiana* was thought to be extinct until a specimen was discovered at the Kadoorie Farm and successfully propagated.

Unique to Hong Kong are the Lady's-slipper Orchid *(Paphiopedilum purpuratum)*, the *Camellia granthamiana* and *Bauhinia blakeana*, Hong Kong's floral emblem.

Introduced Species

Many plants have been introduced into Hong Kong from other countries, often for agricultural purposes. Sometimes this happened so long ago that it is difficult to say whether a plant is truly native or not. However, there are good examples of plants introduced in more recent times. Perhaps one of the best examples of successfully introduced plants is *Lantana camara*, introduced about the middle of the past century as a garden plant. By 1859 it had become naturalised in Happy Valley, growing unattended and spreading rapidly. Before long, it had spread all over Hong Kong, often forming dense thickets. It seems to do very well in sandy areas above beaches, often occurring on quite remote islands. In fact, it is likely to spring up in any area where there is a waste patch of ground. Its ability to spread probably results from its black berry-like fruits that are eaten by birds. The seeds are carried everywhere by them.

Several grasses have been introduced in recent years and are spreading, for example the Southern Sand Bur *(Cenchrus echinatus)*, first recorded about 1965 in Pokfulam Road. Since that time it has spread to the New Territories. It is especially common along railway lines and its spread is facilitated by the burs on the fruit which catch on animals' fur. Another introduced grass is *Panicum maximum*, especially common on building sites. It is often the first coloniser of cleared areas. Even Korean Lawn Grass *(Zoysia japonica)* has escaped from gardens and race track

and can be found growing wild.

The Hong Kong Herbarium on the ninth floor of the New World Centre in Tsim Sha Tsui has a collection of pressed specimens. The collection, originally started in 1878, has 33,300 specimens and 2,594 species and varieties recorded in Hong Kong, as well as some 2,500 specimens from neighbouring countries. It offers a very helpful plant identification service to members of the public.

Walking in Hong Kong

To enjoy walking, you must be comfortably clad. Remember that walking in summer unprotected from the sun can lead to sun stroke and heat stroke. Take a hat if you need one. Good shoes are essential. Wear tennis or sports shoes with good soles to grip the ground on rough pathways. A small haversack is useful, especially to carry something to drink. An umbrella can be helpful, as it protects against both sun and rain. Finally, remember that picking plants is destroying the rich heritage that we have here in Hong Kong. Anyway, many plants are legally protected and you can be prosecuted for collecting them. Don't be tempted to remove them from their natural habitat, but leave them so that others may enjoy them too.

Plant Identification

Plants are classified according to species. The characteristics which define a species in plants are the structure of the flowers, shape and arrangements of leaves, and details such as being hairy or smooth, having prickles or spines, etc.

The system of Linnaeus, the Swedish botanist, is generally used in naming species. The plant is given two Latin or Greek names. The first name is the genus. It defines the general characteristics of the plant that may be shared by several species. The second name is particular to the species. It defines an individual type within the genus. Often the second name describes the character that differentiates it from other members of the genus. For example, 'pilosa' means hairy, while 'repens' means a creeping plant. Thus, *Bidens pilosa* is the Hairy Bur-Marigold while *Bidens bipinnata* has a bipinnate (twice-divided) leaf.

Difficulties sometimes arise in defining a species. Some individuals may show distinct characteristics but they are not thought to be of sufficient importance to make a new species. Then a variety name is given. It can be a matter of opinion of the systematists involved and they do not always agree.

Classification of Plants

This is an attempt to group plant species so as to show their natural relationships. Different species of the same genus are obviously closely related and similarly some genera have common characteristics. They are grouped together in the same Family. The suffix 'aceae' is nearly always used for the ending of Family names. For example, Rosaceae is the Family which includes species of the genus *Rosa* (the wild roses) along with various other genera such as *Prunus* (apricots, peaches, cherries and plums), *Pyrus* (apples and pears), *Eriobotrya* (loquats) and *Rubus* (raspberries).

The next thing is to look at plant Family relationships. What common characteristics do certain Families share? For example, the Families Mimosaceae (Acacia Family), Papilionaceae (Sweet Pea Family) and Caesalpiniaceae (Bauhinia Family) all have much in common with the Rosaceae and so are grouped together in what is called an Order, in this case the Rosales. There are many orders of flowering plants and these are collected into two major groups called Classes. These two are Monocotyledons and Dicotyledons. Their distinguishing characteristics are shown below:

Class Monocotyledons
1) Embryo of seed has one seed leaf (cotyledon)
2) Roots are fibrous or adventitious (borne on the stem or leaves)
3) Stem usually unbranched
4) Stem does not thicken by secondary growth
5) Leaves have parallel veins
6) Flower parts are in whorls of three

Class Dicotyledons
1) Embryo of seed has two seed leaves (cotyledons)
2) A single, deep rooting, tap root is formed that bears lateral roots
3) Stem usually much branched
4) Stem thickens by secondary growth
5) Leaves have net veins
6) Flower parts are in whorls of two, four or five

12

In classifying plants one looks for natural groups in which the members are linked by descent. Where affinities occur, plants are placed together in the same group. The greater the number of affinities, the more likely it is that the classification is truly natural. It is never wise or safe to base a natural classification on one characteristic alone.

There are two major groups of seed plants: the flowering plants, or Angiospermae, and the cone-forming plants, or Gymnospermae. Together they form a group called the Spermatophyta. Flowering plants produce seeds enclosed in a protective case called the ovary which, associated with other structures, form floral whorls that constitute a flower. Gymnospermae are those whose seeds are exposed (usually on the surface of a scale). Cones, a collection of seed-bearing scales, are formed. This group of plants includes Pines, Cedars, Cypresses, Junipers, etc., and are usually referred to as conifers.

Other Plant Divisions

There are various ways of dividing up the main groups of Flowering Plants. As well as the two classes usually defined, the Monocotyledons and the Dicotyledons, higher levels of classification have also been suggested. The Hutchison system, for example, is to make two main Divisions: Lignosae and Herbaceae.

Lignosae
The Lignosae include all the woody plants, those which are capable of thickening their roots and stems by secondary growth. The stems and branches persist from one year to the next. If the leaves fall in the winter, or in dry periods in the tropics, such woody plants are called deciduous. If the leaves last longer than a year, the plant is said to be evergreen. This is so of many Hong Kong trees. The evergreens have to survive the dry autumn period in Hong Kong, so their leaves are specially modified to reduce loss of water vapour. Such leaves have thick surface coatings and a leathery texture, with pores hidden or protected by hairs, and are called xerophytic. Xerophytes are plants modified to survive under dry conditions and many of Hong Kong's trees and shrubs come into this category. They are termed woody perennials and include a large number of the Dicotyledons, but no Monocotyledons.

Herbaceae
Herbaceae include plants where the above-ground parts die down at the end of the hot season. They never become really woody as the result of secondary growth. This division includes some of the Dicotyledons and all the Monocotyledons. They are often generally categorised by their life cycle as follows —
Ephemerals: these carry out several life cycles in one season. They grow, flower and form seed very quickly. This group includes many common weeds such as Shepherd's Purse (*Capsella bursa-pastoris*).
Annuals: these require one season to complete their life cycle. They leave seed behind for the following year.

Biennials: these require two years to complete their life cycle. They do not flower in the first year, usually wintering by means of underground parts, e.g. beetroot, carrot.

Herbaceous Perennials: these live for many years, flowering annually. They perennate by means of underground parts such as bulbs, corms and rhizomes.

The Flower

This is the most important part of a plant for classification. The features of flowers are constant and do not vary as much as the purely vegetative parts, such as leaves, whose size and even shape can vary enormously, even in the same species, according to conditions.

The flower is a leafy shoot which has become much altered for the purpose of reproduction. Its function is to produce seeds that initiate the next generation. The seeds are enclosed within the fruit, at least when first formed. The fruit may be succulent or dry.

The young seed is called an ovule. After pollination and fertilisation, it becomes a seed. If fertilisation fails the ovule usually withers and dies. The fully-formed seed contains an embryo (an ovule does not) which grows into a fully-formed plant when the seed germinates. The ovules are borne inside a modified floral leaf called a carpel. Commonly, several carpels are fused together to form an ovary. After fertilisation, the ovary develops into the fruit, inside which the seeds are found.

The main parts of a flower include an axis, consisting of a flower stalk terminating in a swollen portion, the receptacle, bearing the remaining parts of the flower called floral leaves. In primitive flowers the floral leaves are arranged spirally on the receptacle but in more advanced flowers they are in rings or whorls. There are at least four whorls of floral leaves.

1) Sepals, which together form the Calyx. They are green and protect the inner parts of the flower when in bud.

2) Petals, often brightly-coloured and strongly-perfumed to attract insects to bring about cross-pollination. The petals together form the Corolla.

3) Stamens, the male reproductive organs producing pollen grains in four sacs in a head-like structure called an anther. The anther has a stalk called a filament. When ripe, the anther splits down each side to free the pollen grains to be carried by wind or insects to the receptive stigma of the female part of the same or another flower in the process of pollination.

4) Carpels *(Fig. 1)* enclose and bear the ovules, which may be regarded as female structures. When separate

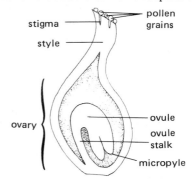

Fig. 1 Carpel of Buttercup

14

from each other (free) the carpels show three distinct parts. These are the ovary, a basal hollow part containing the ovules, the style, an upper elongated part that connects with the third part, the stigma, at its tip. The stigma is often knob-like and sticky to receive pollen grains. Carpels are often joined together in various ways to form a syncarpous ovary which can be seen in the Lily, Violet and Hibiscus (Figs. 2, 3, 4). In syncarpous ovaries, the styles are often free. By counting them, it is possible to determine the number of carpels. If the styles are fused, the stigma is commonly lobed, the number of lobes also corresponding to the number of carpels.

In pollination, the pollen grains are transferred from the anther of the stamen to the stigma of the carpel. This process is followed by fertilisation, when the pollen grain puts out a tube that grows into the stigma and down the style to the ovary. The pollen tube seeks out an ovule and penetrates into it, releasing two male nuclei as fertilising agents. One of these fuses with an ovum (egg cell) in the ovule which then develops into the embryo plant found inside the seed. The other male nucleus fuses with a female nucleus to form a structure that gives rise to a storage tissue of the seed called the endosperm. In many seeds, this becomes largely replaced by the growth of the embryo, although in some it remains as a food store to be drawn upon during germination. This unusual double fertilisation is typical of the flowering plants and does not occur in the same way in Gymnosperms.

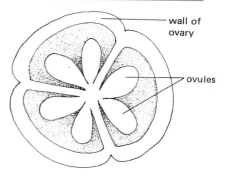

Fig. 2 Syncarpous ovary of Lily

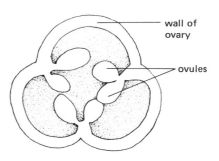

Fig. 3 Syncarpous ovary of Violet

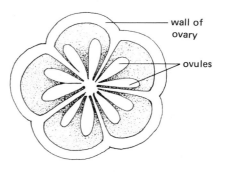

Fig. 4 Syncarpous ovary of Hibiscus

A typical example of a dicotyledonous flower is that of Hong Kong's emblem, *Bauhinia blakeana (Fig. 5)*. In a longitudinal section, the flower stalk can be seen terminating in a bulbous receptacle bearing the floral leaves. To the outside of the flower is a whorl of five sepals, joined into a single structure that splits down one side. Inside the sepals is a whorl of five free crimson-red petals. The one at the back of the flower has a darker centre than the rest, as if overlaid with crimson. There are five stamens, alternating with the petals, with their anthers arching upwards on long filaments. In the very centre of the receptacle is a single elongated carpel, green in colour. Inside, it bears a row of ovules suspended from the upper side of the carpel. There is a terminal style and a knob-like stigma. It is quite a large flower, about 13 cm in diameter, so is easy to examine. One curious thing about this Bauhinia is that it never sets seed. It presumably has some incompatibility factors that check the growth of its pollen tubes. This is not unknown in some fruit trees, such as cherries and plums. All the trees of *B. blakeana* that have been planted in Hong Kong have arisen by vegetative propagation from one original specimen that was discovered by the Fathers of the Missions Etrangers at Pokfulam, growing near the ruins of a house on the seashore. It can now be found planted in many parks and gardens throughout Hong Kong.

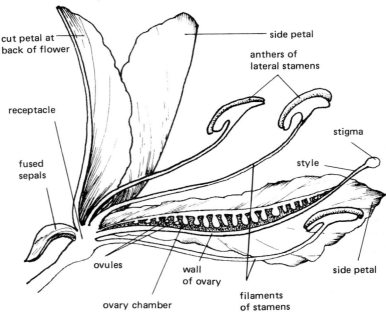

cut petal at back of flower

side petal

anthers of lateral stamens

receptacle

stigma

fused sepals

style

ovules

wall of ovary

side petal

ovary chamber

filaments of stamens

Fig. 5 Dicotyledonous flower cut in half

Types of Flower

In looking at flower structure, it is most important to notice the relationship of the flower parts to the ovary. If the flower parts (sepals, petals, and stamens) are placed on the receptacle below the ovary, the flower is said to be hypogynous, and the ovary is superior *(Fig. 6)*. This is so of most flowers, e.g., Lily, Buttercup, Sweet Pea, etc. However, there are some more advanced groups where the flower parts are placed on top of the ovary and the flower is said to be epigynous and the ovary is inferior, e.g., Chinese New Year Lily *(Narcissus tazetta)*, Amaryllis species and the St John's Lily *(Crinum asiaticum) (Fig. 7)*. An inbetween type also occurs, where the flower parts are arranged around the ovary on the rim of a cup-shaped receptacle. This type of flower is termed perigynous, but the ovary is still regarded as superior, which it is in relation to the position on the receptacle *(Fig. 8)*.

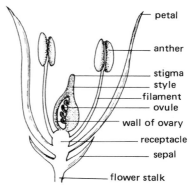

Fig. 6 Hypogynous flower: the ovary is superior

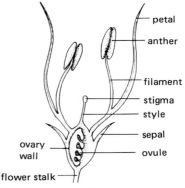

Fig. 7 Epigynous flower: the ovary is inferior

The Inflorescence

This is the term applied to a group of flowers that are all borne on one main stem. Of course, sometimes there is only one flower, as in the Violet or the Tulip, and such inflorescences are called solitary, but generally there are a number of flowers arranged in various ways. The two basic types of arrangement are the raceme (a racemose inflorescence) and the cyme (a cymose inflorescence).

In a raceme *(Fig. 9)* the oldest

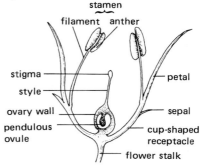

Fig. 8 Perigynous flower: the ovary is superior

17

flowers are at the base of the main axis that bears them and the youngest at the tip. The flowers open from the base upwards and the tip of the raceme continues to grow indefinitely and produce more flowers. There are many common examples, such as the Hyacinth, some Lilies and many Orchids.

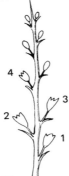

Fig. 9 A raceme

In a cyme, the axis bearing the flowers is terminated by a flower and is therefore of definite growth. Additional flowers open below the first flower and may be borne in pairs (a dichasial cyme) (Fig. 10) or singly (a monochasial cyme) (Fig. 11).

The raceme gives rise to various modifications. If the flowers lack a stalk, it is called a spike (Fig. 12). If the main axis is branched, it is a panicle (Fig. 13). Where the flowers are attached at the same level it is an umbel (Fig. 14). The latter type of branching may be repeated more than once, to form a compound umbel (Fig. 15).

Types of inflorescence must have evolved in relation to insect behaviour, as insects such as bees normally visit racemes by starting at the bottom and moving upwards from flower to flower. This favours cross-pollination where the stamens ripen before the stigmas, which is common. Flowers that have just opened, high up on the raceme, will be shedding pollen. Thus, when the bee leaves the inflorescence, it has just become charged with pollen. On visiting a different raceme, if the flowers at the base are old, their stigmas will be ripe and ready to receive the pollen from the bee. In this way, crossing of different individuals is achieved.

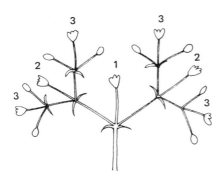

Fig. 10 A dichasial cyme

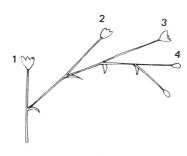

Fig. 11 A monochasial cyme

18

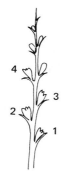

Fig. 12 A spike

Fig. 13 A panicle

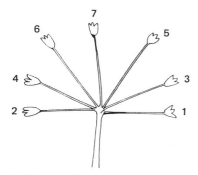

Fig. 14 An umbel

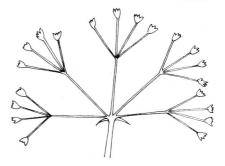

Fig. 15 A compound umbel

Hong Kong Plant Communities

Groups of plants growing together and recognisable as a distinct unit of vegetation are called plant communities. The three major plant communities are woodland, scrubland, and grassland. Of lesser importance are the freshwater and marine communities.

The plant community that covered Hong Kong's land area in the past was evergreen or semideciduous forest. Yet today at least 60 per cent of the land surface is grassland and scrubland. The forests seem largely to have gone. Man's interference with the natural vegetation around him is responsible for this. Nevertheless, remnants of our bygone forests still persist in steep ravines, protected from man's influence by their precipitous position as well as their moist winter microclimate.

There are also small but well-developed woodlands close to many of the older villages and temples in Hong Kong. These are the *fung shui* woods that have been preserved by the villagers to give the village good harmony.

According to its climate, Hong Kong should have humid to semi-humid tropical rain forest as its vegetation. However, since it lies on the northern limit of tropical forest, it has a mixed type of woodland, with both tropical rain forest species as well as those of warm temperate climates. Tropical rain forest species include members of the Moraceae family with its many species of figs *(Ficus)*, such as the Chinese Banyan *(F. microcarpa)*, the Common Red-stem Fig *(F. variegata*, variety *Chlorocarpa)*, the Common Yellow-stem Fig *(F. fistulosa)* and the Rough-leaved Stem Fig *(F. hispida)*. Of the warm temperate forest species, often referred to as evergreen broad-leafed forest types, we have members of the Oak Family (Fagaceae) and the Laurel Family (Lauraceae). In the former family are many species of Oaks *(Quercus)*, Chestnuts *(Castanopsis)* and *Lithocarpus*, while in the latter are species of Camphor *(Cinnamomum)*, *Litsea* and *Machilus*. This oak-laurel forest is typical of our neighbouring provinces of China in upland areas, as well as the high country of Vietnam, Thailand, Burma, Taiwan and Borneo. In *fung shui* woods, the tree flora is often enriched by the planting of the Joss Stick Tree *(Aquilaria sinensis)*, Longan or Dragon's Eye *(Euphoria longan)*, Litchi *(Litchi chinensis)*, Camphor tree *(Cinnamomum camphora)*, Rose-apple *(Syzygium jambos)* and clumps of large bamboos, so these woods are not entirely natural.

Reafforestation, begun in 1842, has generated new forest growths and introduced large areas of artificial woodland. The species used are mainly *Castanopsis fissa* and Chinese Red Pine *(Pinus massoniana)*, both native trees, and the Slash Pine *(Pinus elliottii)*, Brisbane Box *(Tristania conferta)* and *Acacia confusa* which are all introduced species.

When forests are denuded, the deep rich soils are soon eroded by rains. And where the ground is sloping and exposed to the wind, the resulting shallow soil layer becomes unsuitable for the development of tree seedlings and can only support shallow-rooted plants adapted to live in exposed positions. Grasses fill this role well. Hence grassland soon replaces woodland.

Most grassland areas in Hong Kong include some shrubs, e.g. False Tea *(Eurya chinensis)*, Spiny Date-palm *(Phoenix hanceana)*, Dwarf Mountain Pine or Hong Kong Heather *(Baeckea frutescens)* and Mountain Bush Fig *(Ficus variolosa)*, etc. The existence of these shrubs depends on the depth of the soil, the degree of shelter and the water supply. Even a few boulders may provide a micro-habitat that allows survival. A hazard to many plants is hill fires, and those shrubs that can stand up to them are those with their growing points well insulated by surrounding leaves, e.g. *Phoenix hanceana*, or which can develop new growing points from beneath the soil at the base of the plant after damage, e.g. the Hong Kong Hawthorn *(Rhaphiolepis indica)* and *Gordonia axillaris*. Buried seed will also survive fire.

In time grassland may be transformed into scrubland if fires are not too frequent and the activities of man are reduced. If this occurs shrubs such as Rose Myrtle (Rhodomyrtus tomentosa) may form a continuous cover. The shrubs provide shelter for smaller herbaceous plants and climbers, such as various species of Smilax, and at length seedlings of forest trees. After some time, woodland may replace the scrubland. This appears to be happening in several areas on Hong Kong island, such as on Violet Hill where there is a mixture of typical scrubland and woodland species, although the trees have not reached any considerable size. Thus, the relationship between grassland, scrubland and woodland is a dynamic one, depending on a number of factors. If the interference is reduced, the trend will be from grassland to scrubland and finally to woodland. This is a good example of plant succession.

Freshwater communities are found along the many mountain streams in Hong Kong. These streams may be raging torrents in the summer, but are often reduced to a mere trickle in the dry, winter months. Therefore many of the typical aquatic plants seen elsewhere in the world are not to be found. However, plants which characteristically grow on stream banks and on exposed stream beds are present. These include the genera Hydrocotyle, Ludwigia, Polygonum, Acorus and Eriocaulon, while Vallisneria spiralis may be found as a submerged plant. Plants floating on the water include the Water Hyacinth (Eichornia crassipes), the aquatic ferns Azolla pinnata and Salvinia natans, and several Duckweeds.

The marine plant communities may be divided into sandy, rocky and muddy shores. One often finds plants growing in sand on the former. These may include Ipomoea braziliensis, Vitex rotundifolia, Spinifex littoreus and Wedelia prostrata. At the back of the beach there may be shrubs of the Sea Lettuce (Scaevola sericea), Clerodendrum inerme and the Screw Pine (Pandanus tectorius) and still further inland trees of Hibiscus tiliaceus, Macaranga tanarius and Cerbera manghas.

At the back of rocky shores, creepers such as Asparagus cochinchinensis and Morinda umbellata are common, and shrubs such as Scaevola sericea, Pandanus tectorius and Phoenix hanceana are present as on sandy shores. Muddy shores give rise to an interesting dwarf mangrove community of Avicennia marina, Bruguiera conjugata and Aegiceras corniculatum, plus some others.

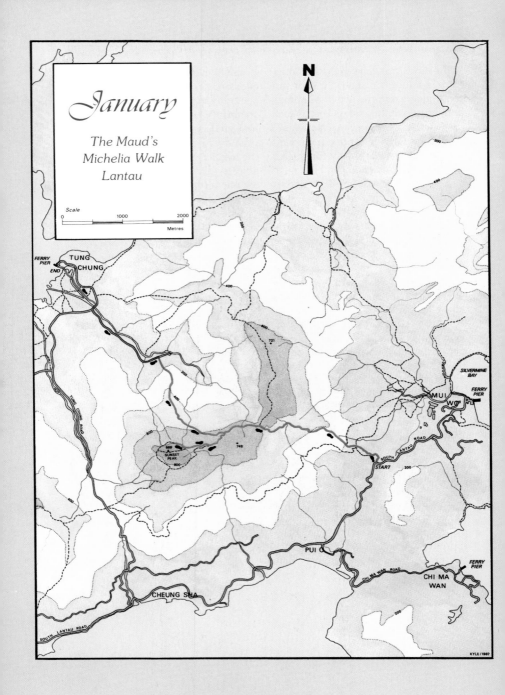

N

January

The Maud's
Michelia Walk
Lantau

Scale

0   1000   2000
Metres

FERRY PIER
END
TUNG CHUNG

TUNG CHUNG ROAD

SOUTH LANTAU ROAD

SUNSET PEAK

START

SOUTH LANTAU ROAD

SILVERMINE BAY
FERRY PIER

MUI WO

PUI O

CHEUNG SHA

CHI MA WAN ROAD

CHI MA WAN

FERRY PIER

KYLE / 1987

January

The Maud's Michelia Walk
Silvermine Bay to Tung Chung
via Sunset Peak, Lantau
Time: 4 — 5 hours

The route in brief

T he rare evergreen tree called
Maud's Michelia, with its creamy
white flowers looking very much like
Magnolia blossoms, is best seen on
the island of Lantau in January when
it is flowering. The hillsides and
woodlands below Sunset Peak take
on a bridal look as the trees with
their crown of blossoms stand out for
miles around.

From Central district, take the
ferry to Silvermine Bay then board a
bus for Pui O. Get off at Nam Shan
at the top of a hill about half-way to
Pui O. Walk on from the bus stop
and then take the forestry road which
you will see on your right. After about
100 metres there is a path leading to
the right through trees. Follow it past
a helipad to a crossing of four paths.
Keep straight on up the hill. The path
follows the contour of the mountain
for some way up to a saddle between
two peaks. Cross the saddle and follow the contour path up the other
side of the mountain to a fork. Turn
left up to some hill bungalows. At
the next fork turn right. About 200
metres along this path you will find
the Maud's Michelia. Return past the
bungalows until there is a left turning
to Tung Chung. Follow this path
down to a road. Turn left into the
road and follow it to a T-junction with
another road that leads to Tung
Chung. Cross the road and follow the
waterway to Tung Chung. Buses run
from Tung Chung back to Silvermine
Bay.

The Walk

From the point where four ways meet, the path you are on climbs steadily through an artificial woodland of Acacia *(Acacia confusa)* and Chinese Red Pine *(Pinus massoniana)*. The under-shrubs which grow in this wood are typical scrubland plants normally found on exposed hillsides; this shows that the woodland is not natural. The Hairy-fruited Abacus Plant *(Glochidion eriocarpum)* is a low, hairy shrub with alternate oval leaves which are red when young. The flowers are unisexual, the male yellow and the female green. The fruit, conspicuous at this time of year, is a reddish-pink globose capsule divided into five segments which, when split open, reveal shiny coral-red seeds. This plant is also known as the Red-haired Marntau because the fruit resembles *marntau*, a type of bread baked into small round loaves.

Other hillside shrubs found below the trees include False Tea *(Eurya chinensis)*, Daphniphyllum calycinum and Rough-leaved Holly *(Ilex asprella)*. *E. chinensis* has many branches and small, alternate leaves with finely serrated margins. It blossoms from December to January, producing tiny, white bell-like flowers with a strong unpleasant odour evidently attractive to many small insects. Several other *Eurya* species occur along the path. One is *E. ciliata*. It does not appear to be listed in the *Hong Kong Check List*. *E. ciliata* is similar in appearance to *E. chinensis* but the stem and buds are covered with a thick growth of soft, light brown hairs. *Ciliata* refers to this characteristic. *Daphniphyllum calycinum*, called Red Cow's Ear by the Chinese, has spirally arranged oval leaves, reddish stalks and veins. It grows to a height of five metres and flowers in spring.

Ilex asprella can reach a height of eight metres or more, though it is commonly the size of a shrub here. When it attains the size of a tree it has a smooth greenish-grey trunk and hairy greenish-brown branches with short spurs. The simple, alternate leaves are rather papery with finely serrated margins and pointed tips. In March it produces tiny white flowers which resemble miniature cherry blossoms. The fruit is a black berry. The root and wood are used in Chinese medicine for treating influenza and tonsilitis. *Mikania guaco*, a climber, can be seen among the pines, often extensively covering the shrubs like a blanket. At this time of the year it is fruiting.

A typical hillside herb found in the

Eurya ciliata

24

Red Cow's Ear
Daphniphyllum calycinum

woods is the Angle-stemmed Hedyotis *(Hedyotis acutangula)*, a member of the Family Rubiaceae which is well represented in Hong Kong. *H. acutangula*, one of fifteen native species of the genus, has pairs of simple, opposite leaves without stalks. A characteristic of this species is the square stem; at the corners are projecting rims of green tissue which must assist the plant in photosynthesis, the process by which plants manufacture sugar from carbon dioxide and water in the leaves and other green parts. Tiny white flowers in dense cymose groups appear later in the year. Another species of *Hedyotis* which occurs in the wood is *H. hedyotidea*, which has smaller leaves than the other species, arranged in the same way on a square but not flanged stem. At this time of the year it will have small, round, brown fruits.

Schizoloma ensifolium, a fern of variable habit, is among the typical ground plants seen in the woods. Its leaves are divided once into a number of leaflets which are arranged in two rows on either side of the midrib of the leaf. Up to eight pairs of leaflets are common in this fern in large specimens. Some fronds may be fertile, forming elongate groups of sporangia at the margin. The sporangia produce tiny dust-like spores (reproductive bodies) that are dispersed by the wind. The fronds rise close together on a creeping stem that is covered with many narrow scales, called a rhizome.

Leaving the Acacia-Pine woods behind, you soon come to a point where, on a clear day, you can command an excellent view of Silvermine Bay and the Chi Ma Wan Peninsula.

The ascending path now follows the side of the hill, and you look down on Cheung Sha and Pui O. Now the vegetation has changed and you are passing through hill scrubland. False Tea is especially abundant in the areas around small streams in the valleys. Among the most common shrubs are Wild Coffee (Psychotria rubra) and Wild Mowtan Peony (Melastoma candidum).

P. rubra (see photograph on p. 32) is a true woodland shrub which grows up to two metres high. The simple, oblong leaves are in opposite

Angle-stemmed Hedyotis
Hedyotis acutangula

pairs and vary in size. *P. rubra* bears a strong resemblance to the true coffee plant but its flowers are much smaller and are creamy white; male and female flowers occur on different plants. The flowers are followed by clusters of berry-like fruits which are green at first, later turning orange and finally red. The true coffee plant has dark brown fruits.

M. candidum is an erect shrub about one metre high with simple, opposite leaves that have prominent longitudinal veins. The branches and leaves are covered with silky white hairs. This plant blooms from May to July, usually with three showy purplish-pink flowers occurring together at the end of a branch. Five of the ten anthers (the part of the stamen that produces pollen in the flower) are curiously modified so that the part of them termed the connective is extended into a long, curved, purple structure. When insects alight on it, the pollen sacs above come into contact with their back, ensuring cross-pollination. The specimens of *M. candidum* seen along this path are often stunted, apparently suffering from exposure.

Climbing up the shrubs and the stunted trees is the Glittering-leaved Millettia *(Millettia nitida)*, one of eight species of the genus that is found in Hong Kong belonging to the Pea Family (Papilionaceae). A tall, woody climber, the young stems and shoots are covered with short, rust-coloured hairs that later fall off. The leaves are alternate and pinnately compound (the leaflets are arranged in two rows on either side of the midrib), being divided into five leaflets.

As the common name suggests the upper leaf surface is smooth and shiny. Dense terminal clusters of purplish-pink flowers, like those of a Sweet Pea, appear in July. The fruit is a hairy pod.

The most common grass on this upland path is the Sword Grass *(Miscanthus floridulus)* (see photograph on p. 32). At this time of year the inflorescences have dried up and look white and fluffy. Another common grass is the Wild Citronella-grass *(Cymbopogon tortilis)*. It has a tufted look because the shoots, clumped together in groups, grow closely at the lower ends but spread out above. The leaf blade is long and narrow and the flowers are small, with awns. Hinds' Cane *(Arundinaria hindsii)*, a tall, bamboo-like grass, is also found on this path. This native grass can grow up to five metres high but here it is much shorter. The straight green stems bear between four and ten strap-shaped leaves with sharply pointed tips in two alternate rows. The inflorescence is a panicle with tiers of branches.

Two species of Aster — the White Bush Aster *(Aster baccharoides)* and the White Mountain Aster *(Aster ageratoides)* — are also quite common. It is not easy to distinguish between them. Both occur at high elevations on windy slopes and have small daisy-like flower-heads in dense groups and ovate leaves with toothed margins. White Mountain Aster is generally taller, however, growing to one metre in height while the White Bush Aster is only about 60 cms tall.

Anywhere along the path you may find a small herb with attractive pink

27

White Mountain Aster
Aster ageratoides

flowers. This is the Creeping Melastoma *(Melastoma dodecandrum)*. It has opposite, simple leaves, shiny and hairless, with three prominent veins. The fruit is a small, purple, edible berry. This plant flowers in May, but may be seen in bloom at other times of the year. Another frequently seen plant is the Nodding Club-moss *(Lycopodium cernuum)*, not a true fern but a fern ally. It has forking branches covered densely with spirally arranged, almost linear leaves. Some branches are horizontal and sprout roots. The erect branches terminate in downwardly directed cones, having a nodding appearance, hence the common name.

In one place the hillside path forks. You may take either route as the two paths soon unite again. The left fork is steeper but shorter. At length, after crossing a stream where there is a clump of False Tea, the path climbs up to a saddle in the mountains. This is a good place to picnic as the views are superb. In one direction you look down to the south-east side of Lantau, and in the other the north-west side towards Tung Chung. After reaching the saddle, follow the path that crosses it and leads to the left around and up the mountain on the other side. You have now left the south-east side of the central mountain range on Lantau and are on the north-west side. As you follow the path, Tung Chung will come into view. Shek Lap Kok Island may be seen clearly beyond.

After five to ten minutes' walk from the saddle, you will come to another fork; the right-hand fork leads downhill to Tung Chung and takes about two and a half hours. This is the path you take on your return journey. To reach the site where Maud's Michelia *(Michelia maudiae)* grows, you must take the left fork, and continue gently upwards. After a little while you will come to some hill bungalows. The path leads up between them. Carry on until you come to a fork well beyond the bungalows. Take the right one. This path goes all the way round Sunset Peak and joins itself again. It soon leaves the open hillside and begins to descend through an area of low woodland. At one point you cross a small stream. Perhaps 30-40 metres beyond the stream on your left, a little way up the hillside, are several bushes of Maud's Michelia.

A small evergreen tree about five metres high, *M. maudiae* (see photograph on p. 32) has dark-green, leathery, oval leaves pointed at both ends, with glossy, pale-green margins. In January the trees are covered by large, creamy-white flowers, in size and appearance resembling the Magnolia, to which they are closely related. The petals are oval- to ob-

long-shaped, rather pointed at the tips. There are many pinkish-yellow stamens around a number of green ovaries that stick up above them in the centre of the flower. The fruit is an aggregate of pod-like follicles which split open down one side only (a true pod splits open down both sides).

Maud's Michelia was discovered and first described by S.T. Dunn, superintendent from 1903 to 1910 of Hong Kong's Botanical and Forestry Department, who named the plant in honour of his wife. In January the white patches of their flowers may be easily picked out from a good vantage point. However the plant is quite rare, having been recorded at only one or two other places in Hong Kong.

Having seen Maud's Michelia you can now retrace your steps to the bungalows. Or if you wish, follow the path right round Sunset Peak, which brings you back to your starting point, though this will take much longer. Go down the path between the bungalows and follow the hill path you came up on until you get to the turning, now on your left, with the signpost saying it is 2½ hours' walk to Tung Chung. Take this left turning. This path descends down the hillside. You are on the north-west side of Sunset Peak, well protected from monsoon winds. Here the vegetation is much richer and you soon enter an area of lush woodland.

Pithecellobium lucidum, a small evergreen tree of the Family Mimosaceae, can be seen here. Its branches are covered with rust-brown hairs that bear large multi-segmented leaves arranged in two alternating rows. The flowers are yellowish, grouped into small globose heads. Each flower gives rise to a curious pod that is twisted into a circle and splits into two valves to set free large seeds.

Another tree that can be seen is the Yellow Basket-willow *(Engelhardtia chrysolepis)*, a large deciduous tree with smooth, brown bark, and alternate bipinnate leaves. It may still bear leaves at this time of the year. Later in the year catkins appear, male and female separate, but on the same tree. The female catkins form long drooping spikes which, when ripe, bear little nuts. *E. chrysolepis* is in the family Juglandaceae to which the walnut *(Juglans regia)* belongs.

At one part of the hillside path, still in the wooded area, there is a small stream. In wet weather it flows across the path, and even in January, a fairly dry month, the soil may be very wet. Here one finds moisture-loving plants such as ferns, and delicate herbs that enjoy the shade. One such plant is Pipewort, a species of *Eriocaulon* that usually thrives in marshy areas or on the sides of streams. It has a rosette of slender, tapering leaves and four pairs of small white flowers at the ends of stems. The white appearance is due to bracts among the flowers. There are at least eight species of this genus in Hong Kong.

In this wet area the insectivorous plant Sundew *(Drosera spathulata*, also called *D. loureiri)* is found. Its rosettes of spatula-shaped, cuneate leaves are covered with small sticky tentacles that catch tiny insects. A small shrub found here is *Dichroa fe-brifuga*, a relative of Hydrangea. It is not much more than a metre in height, with large, paired, oval leaves that have serrated edges. At this time of the year the plant is laden with large shimmering mauve-blue fruits with a waxy sheen. Inside are many tiny brown seeds. The root of this plant contains Dichroin which is used to treat fevers.

Another shrub in the wet zone is the Glabrous Pittosporum *(Pittosporum glabratum)*, also about a metre high. It is characterised by its paired, oval, smooth-margined leaves and fragrant, greenish-yellow flowers. In January it bears large dark-brown fruits which split open into three valves to expose a collection of pillar-box red seeds arranged in three rows. Presumably they are dispersed by animals which are attracted to them by their bright colour.

Growing near *P. glabratum* is *Alpinia stachyodes*, a member of the Zingiberaceae family to which the Ginger plant belongs. *A. stachyodes* is a metre or more in height, with two rows of elongate leaves and oval, red fruits borne in a raceme. The Papery Daphne *(Daphne papyracea)* is another shrub growing in the wet zone. It has alternate, simple oval-shaped leaves and produces strongly-scented pure white flowers in groups of about eight, with no sepals, only four joined petals, and eight stamens. The floral fragrance evokes white lilies.

A rather rare fern, *Gleichenia chinensis Rosenst*, grows in these woods. An underground root-like stem produces large fronds that may have a leaf-stalk taller than a person before it forks. Pairs of lateral 'branches' arise below the tip of the frond and grow to a metre or more in length. These lateral 'branches' bear alternating leaflets in two rows that are deeply lobed. The under-surface of the branches and the mid-veins of leaflets are covered with persistent brown scales.

As you follow the hillside path the woodland gives way to scrubland. There are no less than thirty species of shrubs or stunted trees in this area, proof of the extraordinary diversity of Hong Kong's flora. Among the herbaceous flowering plants seen on the last part of the walk is the Windy Hill Strobilanthes *(Strobilanthes apricus)* with alternate, elliptic, dark green

leaves and attractive blue- to lavender-coloured funnel-shaped flowers borne in the leaf axils. It flowers in autumn and may continue into January. The fruit is an oblong capsule with four seeds.

At length the path you are following gives way to many steps descending to a small road. Turn left into this road and follow it through a pleasant valley. Eventually this road joins the main road that leads to Tung Chung. Perhaps a more pleasant way to the village is to cross the main road and follow the path alongside the artificial waterway through cultivated fields. As Tung Chung and the coast can be seen in the distance you cannot really go wrong.

Windy Hill Strobilanthes
Strobilanthes apricus

31

Maud's Michelia
Michelia maudiae

Maud's Michelia flower

Wild Coffee
Psychotria rubra

Sword Grass
Miscanthus floridulus

Cuban Bast fruit

Cuban Bast flower
Hibiscus tiliaceus

Uvaria
Uvaria microcarpa

Hong Kong Hawthorn
Rhaphiolepis indica

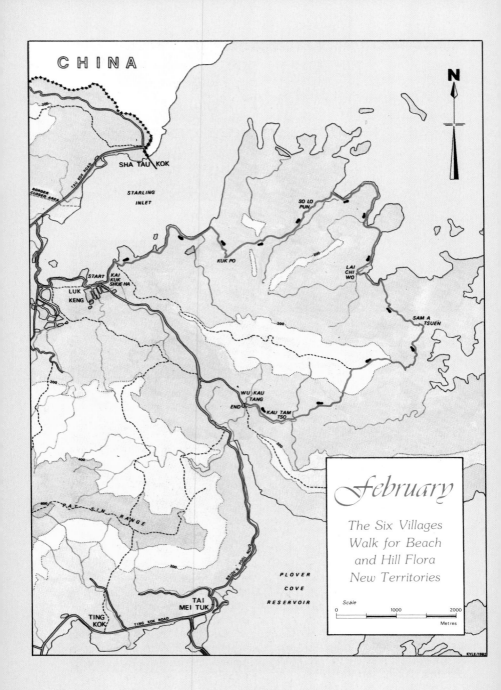

CHINA

N

SHA TAU KOK

TAU KOK ROAD

BORDER
CLOSED AREA

STARLING
INLET

SO LO
PUN

KUK PO

LAI
CHI
WO

START
KAI
KUK
SHUE HA

LUK
KENG

200

SAM A
TSUEN

200

WU KAU
TANG

END
KAU TAM
TSO

200

February

The Six Villages
Walk for Beach
and Hill Flora
New Territories

400

PAT SIN RANGE

200

BRIDE'S POOL ROAD

200

PLOVER

COVE

RESERVOIR

Scale

0   1000   2000

Metres

TAI
MEI TUK

TING
KOK

TING KOK ROAD

KYLE/1982

34

February

The Six Villages Walk for Beach and Hill Flora
Starling Inlet, New Territories
Time: 7 — 8 hours

The route in brief

The variety of flora and scenery found along beach paths, mangrove swamps, hill scrubland and woodland in Starling Inlet and the North-east New Territories is unique for such a small area. To appreciate this rich plant life, head for Tai Po in the New Territories.

From Tai Po you must go by car to Kai Kuk Shu Ha. The bus (No. 75K) goes only as far as Plover Cove Reservoir. In Kai Kuk Shu Ha take a path to the east of the parking area. The path follows the coast, leaving it at one point to cross a headland, but rejoining it on the other side. After crossing a dam, turn right by a group of houses on to a path leading to Kuk Po village. Beyond the group of houses, at the second new house, take a small path on your left that brings you up into woodland. Here take first a right and then a left fork

as the path climbs up to a cutting in the hills.

Cross this cutting and follow the path down the other side on the slopes of a steep valley. Where the path curves to the left, after crossing a stream, leave it and break out of the wood over some former paddy fields on your right. Drop down through several old paddy terraces and you come to a good path that leads to So Lo Pun village. After passing through the village ignore turnings on your right until you come to a dam. Turn right across it and then immediately left on the other side to follow a coastal path. This takes you round a headland to a small bay. Cross the bay, or follow it round if the tide is up. On the far side of the bay, just above the shore, is a good path. Turn left onto it and follow it through to Lai Chi Wo. It crosses a peninsula en route. Leave the village square of Lai Chi Wo by the exit under a large banyan tree. The path follows the coast at first, later turning inland past two large fish ponds. It follows a canal, on your left, for a while. Later take a left turn, and after crossing some former paddy fields you will reach Sam A Tsuen.

After walking past the line of houses that forms the village, cross some more ricefields and turn left on to a path on the other side. This path climbs upwards. Soon you must take a right fork which joins a ridge path. It descends later to join a low-level path in a valley. Turn right along this path and follow it to Kau Tam Tso. Just before the village turn left and carry on along the side of a stream to Wu Kau Tang. From here you can board a lorry bus for Tai Po.

The Walk

This is a fairly long walk but worth the effort. The trees at the beginning of the path include some typical Hong Kong woodland species but once you approach the seashore, typical coastal species such as *Cerbera manghas*, *Pandanus tectorius* and Cuban Bast *(Hibiscus tiliaceus)* are cheek by jowl with the others.

Cuban Bast (see photographs on p. 33) is a medium-sized tree with alternate, heart-shaped leaves that are white underneath. The leaf-stalks and under-side of the leaf veins are reddish. In February downy fruit capsules are in evidence. They split into five valves to set the seeds free. Flowering begins in June, and is abundant. There are five sepals, joined at their base, outside which is an extra whorl of twelve pointed lobes called an epicalyx. The five yellow petals are free (not joined together) and soon fall, and there are many stamens joined together by their stalks into a column. The superior ovary is made up of five joined carpels. The centre of the flower is marked with dark brown and as the petals age they become a reddish-orange colour. This flower is very beautiful when seen against a clear blue sky.

Another typical coastal species common along Starling Inlet is the Sea Lettuce *(Scaevola sericea)*, a spreading shrub growing to about a metre or more in height. The crowns of fresh green leaves crowded together look like certain varieties of lettuce, hence the common name. It has spiral, rather succulent oval-shaped leaves with rounded tips. In June it produces odd-looking white flowers occurring in small groups in the leaf axils and appearing as though half the petals are missing. In fact this is not so; the corolla tube is merely split laterally, the five lobes of the petals spreading out on the one side of the flower to form a landing stage for insects. There are usually two reddish stripes on the corolla. The fruit is a white, fleshy berry, still crowned with the green sepals.

Crotalaria saltiana Andr is a low-growing seashore shrub that bears groups of dark brown fruits in February. Each pod contains about 20 seeds. The pods hang down so that they are vertically aligned with the flowering axis that bears them. In summer this plant has alternate, trifoliate leaves with long stalks. When flowering it is most attractive, with a tall raceme of yellow, pea-like flowers.

As you follow the path along the southern side of Starling Inlet, the land to the south rises gently into hills where typical Hong Kong scrubland species abound. Hong Kong Hawthorn *(Rhaphiolepis indica)* (see photograph on p. 33) is one of the few shrubs that will be seen blooming in February. Another shrub that may just be coming into flower in February, if the weather is warm, is *Maesa perlarius*. It has rather weak branches bearing alternate, oval leaves with clearly toothed margins. The flowers, white and quite small, are borne in clusters on short axillary stems. The flower parts are in whorls of five and have a sweet perfume, like the smell of new-mown hay. *M. perlarius* is not really a hillside shrub, being usually found in damp woodland areas.

Several very spiny shrubs may be seen along this coastal path, including *Scolopia chinensis* and *Atalantia buxifolia*, both of which have large stem spines in the leaf axils. The spines of *S. chinensis* are longer than those of *A. buxifolia*. These large, strong spines with needle-like points protect the plant against herbivorous animals. *Paliurus ramosissimus* is an-other spiny shrub, but in this one the leaves have become modified as spines.

A prickly shrub found along the shore is the Memorial Rose *(Rosa wichuriana)*. It has stems covered with hooked prickles that bear alternate, once-pinnate leaves of five to seven ovate leaflets with finely toothed margins. Where the leaf joins the stem is a pair of pointed stipules that are partly fused to the petiole, a characteristic of the genus Rosa. In March and April the terminal racemes of white or pale pink flowers may be seen. The clusters of small flowers are rather like the rambler roses of European gardens.

Several interesting climbers live along the coastal path. One of these is *Uvaria microcarpa* (see photograph on p. 33), a straggling shrub with simple, alternate leaves, that sends out climbing branches. The stems and leaves have a rusty, furry appearance due to a dense covering of star-shaped hairs. In May or June,

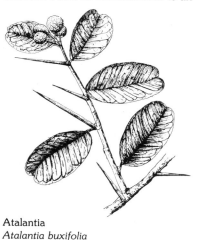

Atalantia
Atalantia buxifolia

Thorny Wingnut
Paliurus ramosissimus

this plant produces artificial-looking flowers with six orange-brown velvety petals in two whorls. There are three joined sepals (floral leaves) below the petals and numerous whorls of stamens in the middle forming a yellow blob; inside these are many free carpels packed closely together. It is a primitive flower, but must be efficient in producing seed, as it is a fairly common plant among the undergrowth of scrubland and in wooded valleys.

A typical coastal climbing plant found all along the path to Kuk Po is the Sea Sword Bean *(Canavalia maritima)*. It climbs by counter-clockwise twisting stems. The leaves are alternate and divided into three leaflets. In February, large, conspicuous brown pods can be seen. The pod has a double ridge down one side and splits open on both sides to shed large, brown seeds. Pink flowers resembling Sweet Pea flowers are formed in late summer.

Close to a picnic site on your left the coastal path leaves the shoreline and climbs to the top of a hill. On the hilltop is a recreation area. Cross it to find the path down to the seashore on the other side. Continue along the coastal path. Here and there on the path you will see typical mangrove swamp plants along the shoreline such as *Kandelia candel, Aegiceras corniculatum* and *Clerodendrum inerme*. The first two are shrubs. *K. candel* will have the characteristic droppers present in February, but will not be flowering. In June it produces umbels of white, star-like flowers. *A. corniculatum* flowers in March and so will be seen in bud in

Aegiceras corniculatum

February. The flower buds are formed in umbels at the tips of the branches. *C. inerme*, a scrambling shrub with long, straggly branches, only flowers in summer. In February you are likely to see only the rounded, brown capsules usually still enclosed within the enlarged, persistent calyx. They split into four valves to set the seed free.

The coastal path leads you over a dam to a group of houses, where you take a right turn inland on to a path leading to Kuk Po village. Beyond the group of houses, and some way before Kuk Po village, look on your left for a small path which winds through some disused paddy fields. Making your way through grassland (there is no path) you will eventually come across the path you need. The path leads into the hills and eventually to So Lo Pun, a deserted village.

As you walk through the grassland, look out for the two most common grasses present: the Sword

Grass (*Miscanthus floridulus*), and the Ciliate Sasagrass (*Microstegium ciliatum*), both growing up to 120 cms tall where undisturbed. Woody Grass (*Imperata cylindrica*) is somewhat smaller and is easily recognised by its long and narrow inflorescence which is white and fluffy. The spikelets bear long, fine, white hairs at the top and bottom. This grass spreads rapidly over wide areas by means of underground runners which survive fire. The leaves are nearly all borne at the stem's base and are very long with rough edges.

Among the various herbs along the side of the path, look for a white variety of *Ageratum conyzoides*. It will be in bloom, and seems to flower almost all the year round. The Moneywort (*Centella asiatica*) forms a carpet to the path, its creeping stems giving rise to rounded leaves with a lobed margin.

The ascending path passes through open woodland of Chinese Red Pine (*Pinus massoniana*). There is a well-defined shrub layer, many members of which are actually typical scrubland species, such as Rose

Ageratum
Ageratum conyzoides

Myrtle *(Rhodomyrtus tomentosa)*, Myrobalan *(Phyllanthus emblica)*, the Hairy-fruited Abacus Plant *(Glochidion eriocarpum)*, Wild Coffee *(Psychotria rubra)* and the two species of *Melastoma (M. candidum* and *M. sanguineum)*. An interesting sub-shrub called False Groundnut *(Desmodium heterocarpon)* is common. It has alternate, hairy, divided leaves, each with three equal leaflets. In February, pointed pods divided into one-seeded segments, may still be present. They are covered by stiff hairs that catch onto animals for dispersal.

This plant flowers from July onwards forming racemes of pink, butterfly-like flowers. It is a member of the Pea Family (Papilionaceae).

As you climb upwards through the wood first take a right and then a left fork. Perhaps the most common tree here is the Pop-gun Seed *(Bridelia monoica)*. It has alternate, oblong leaves; in their axil are one or two conspicuous green fruits which ripen to black. The trunk is a smooth grey-ish-brown with orange-brown slits. Among the trees frequently seen here is *Viburnum sempervirens*, a small

False Groundnut
Desmodium heterocarpon

tree with opposite, simple, ovate leaves distinguishable from the three other local species of *Viburnum* by its leaf veins. The basal ones extend more than three quarters of the leaf's length.

In the denser part of the forest, *Maesa perlarius* and *Uvaria microcarpa* are common. The Wild Raspberry *(Rubus reflexus)*, is also seen everywhere, with its furry, prickly stems and palmately lobed leaves with dark red markings on them. In June it bears typical raspberry fruits which are delicious.

In one part of the wood a stream passes close to the path and there is a small waterfall. In this wet, shady area there is a large specimen of the fern *Microlepia hancei*. It has bipinnately compound giant fronds arising from a creeping rhizome (root-like stem). The fern *Cyclosorus interruptus* (Wild) *H. Ito* is also present here but it has smaller once-divided fronds. It usually occurs by water.

The path soon takes you up out of the wood into open scrubland. Here the vegetation is almost exclusively made up of the False Staghorn Fern *(Dicranopteris linearis)*. Its forking fronds seem to cover every square inch of the hillside. The path climbs steeply and at last reaches a cutting in the hills. Here you have an excellent view of Sha Tau Kok, on the far side of Starling Inlet. Using binoculars you will be able to see the street that marks the border with China. Hong Kong lies on the left of the street, China on the right. The street runs at right angles to the seashore, right through the centre of Sha Tau Kok.

At the top of the path is a crossroads of paths. Go straight over it, ignoring the turnings. On the other side of the cutting, the path starts to descend, following the hillside on the left of a steep valley. Soon you are in woodland again, and on a sunny day you will be glad of the shade. The trees present include most of those described on the way up.

A species of *Glochidion* found here is Wright's Abacus Plant *(G. wrightii)* which can grow to a height of 8 metres. It is closely related to the Hairy-fruited Abacus Plant *(G. eriocarpum)*. *G. wrightii* has alternate, simple leaves like those of *G. eriocarpum* but slightly smaller, and the stems and leaf stalks are reddish coloured. Both species bear fruits that look like abacus beads; the main difference between them is that in *G. eriocarpum* the fruit is divided into five segments, while in *G. wrightii* there are only three. One can see this by cutting the fruit across.

Wild Mussaenda *(Mussaenda erosa)* is another shrub found in the wood. It has simple, ovate hairless leaves in opposite pairs. The flowers are orange-yellow, and some of the outer members of the group have a single sepal expanded to form a large, white leaf-like structure to attract insects. The plant is closely related to the more common *M. pubescens*, or Splash-of-white, and differs from it by having shorter calyx teeth and no hairs.

The woodland path eventually crosses a stream and curves to the left. Do not follow this. Instead break out of the wood to the right where you will find some paddy fields overgrown with Woody Grass (Imperata cylindrica). Proceed in a downward direction over the old rice terraces and you will come to a good path which goes to the deserted village of So Lo Pun. The path is lined by Sword Grass.

So Lo Pun is a good spot for a picnic lunch, but if it is getting late, you should press on to Lai Chi Wo. In So Lo Pun there are various plants that were once cultivated but have since gone wild. One of these is *Kalanchoe flabellatum*. It has thick, fleshy stems and ovate leaves with bluntly lobed margins, arranged in opposite pairs. It may be flowering in February. Watch out for bright orange tubular flowers with four joined petals, eight stamens and four free carpels. When fruiting there are four follicles (fruits that split down one side only). *Kalanchoe* is unusual in that it propagates itself by forming small buds along the leaf margin. These eventually drop off as bulbils that will grow into new plants. From So Lo Pun carry on along the path that goes through the village, ignoring turnings to the right which would take you into a quagmire.

At length the path above the marshy area passes along the side of a stream which is on your right. Along its banks are seashore plants such as Sea Lettuce, Cuban Bast and a species of Wedelia with yellow flowerheads and opposite, simple leaves. Several typical mangrove species occur including the rather rare mangrove fern, *Acrostichum aureum*. Conspicuous in the water is the Common Reed Grass (*Phragmites communis*) with tall fluffy, silvery-grey panicles of flowers.

You eventually come down to a sort of dam that has been built transverse to the valley. Turn right along the dam and cross it. The path appears to continue once you have crossed, but actually reaches a dead-end. Turn left on to the coastal path at the end of the dam which follows the headland. At one point the rocks jut out and if the tide is up you will have to clamber round them. If the tide is out you can walk below the rocks.

Even on this rocky shore where there is little soil a few plants grow, though the struggle for existence is hard. Most of the plants here are low-growing herbs found in rock crevices, for example, *Centella asiatica*, usually found on woodland or hillside paths and a fern, *Sphenomeris chinensis*. The Nodding Club-moss (*Lycopodium cernuum*) also occurs. Tufts of the grass-like leaves of *Liriope spicata* sprout from cracks in the rock. This is a woodland plant that has attractive mauve flowers in spikes looking like lavender. The Mangrove Grass (*Zoysia sinica*) is common on flat areas below high tide.

On the seashore brown seaweeds detached from the rocks are washed up by the tide. Spherical masses of *Colpomenia sinuosa*, looking like brown-coloured human brain, may be seen. The brown Seaweed, *Hydroclathrus clathratus*, forms irregular networks looking almost like open-work sponges. You may see flattened finger-like branches, sandy yellow in colour, of a soft coral.

Once you have rounded the rocky headland you come to a small bay.

You can walk across it if the tide is out, otherwise follow it round. In this bay is a small mangrove community. *Kandelia candel* should be showing the characteristic droppers; the Many-petaled Mangrove *(Bruguiera conjugata)* may be flowering; *Aegiceras corniculatum* may be showing flower buds, and *Avicennia marina* may be seen with its aerial roots sticking up through the mud.

A less common seashore plant found here is the Sea Lavender *(Limonium sinense)*, a perennial herb which has a rosette of fleshy, spoon-shaped leaves with a flattened, white leaf-stalk. A repeatedly branched inflorescence of white-to-yellow flowers occurs in February. There are green bracts among the flowers, and the white sepals persist long after the yellow petals have withered. The flowers may be dried.

Having crossed the bay, you will find a good path above the shoreline. Turn left along it and continue to Lai Chi Wo, the third village on this walk. At first this path crosses the neck of a peninsula of land, coming out into another bay. Follow the coastline of

Sea Lavender
Limonium sinense

43

the bay until you reach the village. Along this coastal path you may see some dried stems sticking up from the ground and bearing interesting fruits. This plant is the Musk Mallow (*Abelmoschus moschatus Medik*). The fruit is a capsule with sharply pointed tips, brown outside and silvery-grey inside, that splits longitudinally into five valves. An annual, the plant dies at the end of the year, leaving behind only the seeds for its survival. The seeds smell like musk and are used in some countries for medicine and for making perfume. By June the plant is well developed with spiral, palmately lobed leaves that have long stalks. Both stems and leaves are covered with rough, stiff hairs. The flowers, large and attractive, are formed singly in the leaf axils from June onwards. There are five bright yellow petals joined at their bases, with a brownish-red centre, and many stamens with their filaments united into a column as in the Hibiscus, to which this plant is closely related.

The village of Lai Chi Wo is inhabited but its population has declined over the years. It has an interesting Tin Hau Temple and a very large Chinese Banyan (*Ficus microcarpa*) in a corner of the village square. An evergreen tree, the Chinese Banyan is easily recognised by the aerial roots hanging from its branches. If they touch the soil they root and form strong supporting structures for the branches. However, the atmosphere in Hong Kong is generally too dry during much of the year for this to happen so the roots just trail in the air like tassels. The leaves of the Chinese Banyan

are alternate and oval-shaped with entire margins. In February it bears small, globose, green figs which turn pink and finally dark red, and are much sought after by birds.

Leave the village square by the exit under the large banyan tree. The path crosses some fields and soon follows the coast. At the side of the path is a spiny tomato-like plant with bright red poisonous fruits. Commonly known as Poisonous Tomato (*Solanum aculeatissimum*), the plant has alternate triangular leaves with shallow lobed margins, and small white flowers resembling those of the tomato plant, which belongs to the same family.

The coastal path at one point leaves the coast and skirts some trees. If you look among the trees you will see some very thick woody vines. This is the white-flowered *Derris alborubra* with alternate once-pinnate leaves with five leaflets. The small wood where it occurs probably has been maintained for generations by the villagers as a *fung shui* wood.

Further along, close to the beach, the path is lined by large trees on the seaside. These are specimens of the Looking Glass Tree (*Heritiera littoralis*), found only along seacoasts as it is spread by a fruit containing a spongy air-filled tissue that allows it to float in sea water. These fruits have a prominent ridge running round them. The tree has spiral, rather thick, leathery, oval leaves with an entire margin. The upper leaf surface is green, smooth and shiny, but the underside has a covering of scales which give it a silvery appearance, hence its common name.

Along the coast are *Cerbera manghas* trees and the spiny shrub *Scolopia chinensis*. Growing in the sand at the top of the beach is the Wide-leaved St John's Lily *(Crinum latifolium)*. The rosettes of these large leaves can hardly be missed. The plant flowers in summer.

Leaving the coast before two large fishponds the path goes inland by a canal. When you come to a junction of paths by an old gnarled tree, take the left and after a while you will come to some neglected ricefields. Across the fields is Sam A Tsuen, the fourth village on this walk. Make your way to the village across the ricefields. Sam A Tsuen is no more than a line of one-storey houses. Carry on past the houses until you reach more disused ricefields. Cross them towards a path on the other side. Turn left. Soon you will climb into typical hill scrubland. Don't miss the right fork leading up a hill. You will eventually pass one or two houses, after which you will walk along a ridge path across a low hill. The path descends to a valley on your left and joins another path low in the valley. Turn right at the junction and carry on towards Kau Tam Tso, the

fifth village on this walk.

The vegetation between Sam A Tsuen and Kau Tam Tso includes most of the shrubs of hill scrubland near Kuk Po. The small, delicate herb, the Skullcap *(Scutellaria indica)*, should be blooming now. The inflorescence is a one-sided raceme of pale mauve flowers spotted with purple. The five petals are joined into a tube, white on the outside, with two main lobes. The upper lobe, made up of four petals, forms a protective hood above the stamens, and the lower one, subdivided into three, forms a landing stage for insects. It has a squarish, purplish hairy stem and simple leaves with round-lobed margins arranged in opposite pairs.

When you reach Kau Tam Tso take a left turn. This path takes you past the village without having to go into it. The path soon follows a stream on your left. After about ten minutes you will reach Wu Kau Tang, the sixth and last village on this walk. Again the path skirts the village and passes through some trees, finally crossing a stream and leading up into a large parking area for cars and buses. From here you can take a lorry bus to Tai Po.

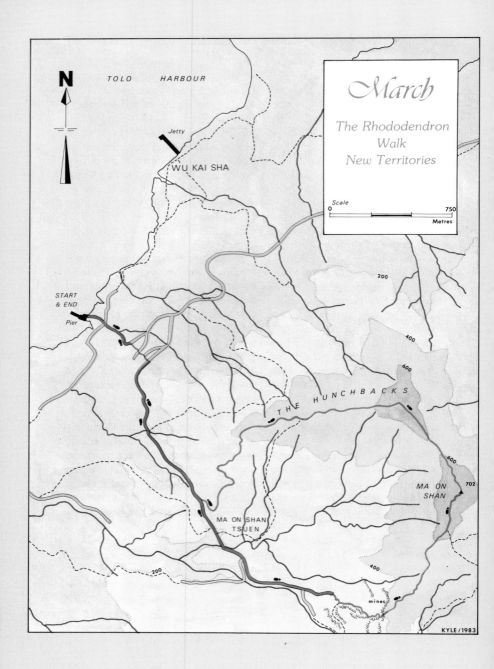

N

TOLO HARBOUR

Jetty

WU KAI SHA

March

The Rhododendron
Walk
New Territories

Scale

0   750

Metres

START
& END

Pier

200

400

600

THE HUNCHBACKS

600

MA ON
SHAN   702

MA ON SHAN
TSUEN

400

200

mines

KYLE/1983

March

The Rhododendron Walk
Ma On Shan, New Territories
Time: 4 — 5 hours

The route in brief

A riot of pink and orange blooms breaks out on the slopes of the Hunchback range of mountains in the New Territories when Rhododendron blossom time comes in March. To see these gorgeous blooms in their natural setting, go to Ma On Shan Tsuen, a former mining village near Tolo Harbour.

Travel by bus, train or car to the Chinese University of Hong Kong and then walk to the jetty to catch the ferry that crosses Tolo Harbour (check ferry schedules beforehand). When you land on the other side of Tolo Harbour, follow the main road going inland from the jetty and when the road forks, take the right. Watch out for a small path on your right a few metres ahead. Take this path which climbs the hillside through woodland crossing two terraces to the road above. Turn right on to this road until you see a sign that says 'Disused Mine'. Turn left along a dirt road here and almost at once branch right. When the dirt road peters out take a hill path on your right which climbs steeply up to the first and lowest peak of the Hunchbacks.

On reaching this peak turn right on to a ridge path running the length of the Hunchbacks to Ma On Shan Peak. The path goes over several crests and dells and is very steep in places. Avoid a left fork towards its end. From the peak the path descends steeply. At the first fork go right, keeping on a high level ridge path and ignoring the descending path. It surmounts several hilltops across a long ridge towards the disused iron mine where it peters out at a landslip. Follow the fringe of this to the right down to a terrace. Make your way through open scrubland to a road below and turn left along it. This road soon joins another on to which you make a right turn. Follow the road over a bridge and past some houses. The walk eventually takes you back to the road you started from, down to the jetty and the ferry ride back to the Chinese University.

47

The Walk

The walk itself is a fairly stiff one, but the climb along the mountain ridge is rewarded by superb views. From the airy crest of the ridge you can see right out to Tolo Harbour and the Eight Fairies Mountain Peaks beyond. The countryside is peaceful and deserted, except possibly for an occasional group of hikers. You will pass through typical hill scrubland forming a backdrop of greenery, with steep woodland on the north side of your path. The best place to stop for a picnic would probably be at the top of Ma On Shan. Take drinks with you as there is no place to buy any, and scarcely a stream on your route until you get back to the village.

On ascending the hillside path shortly after the jetty, you will see a small evergreen tree. This is *Mallotus paniculatus*, commonly called 'Turn-in-the-wind' because the almost diamond-shaped leaves twist to and fro in the wind, showing their white under-surface. This tree does not flower in March, but in August it produces masses of strongly scented, small, creamy white flowers, lacking petals, in catkin-like spikes. The fruit is a three-chambered capsule.

As you ascend the path you will come to at least two terraces which you must cross. There are many steps on the path. At one point there are several trees of Pond Spice *(Litsea glutinosa)*, an evergreen member of the Lauraceae family. It is about 10 metres tall with simple spiral leaves. In May when it flowers the whole tree is full of globular groups of small greenish-yellow blooms. (In the olden

Pond Spice
Litsea glutinosa

days thin slices of wood from this tree were soaked in water to produce a sticky fluid which Chinese ladies used as a hair lacquer.)

After a steep climb the path joins the road from the jetty. Turn right and walk for about a quarter of a mile. The most noticeable shrub here is the Hong Kong Hawthorn *(Rhaphiolepis indica)*, very common on Hong Kong hillsides. It blooms at this time of year. The Hong Kong Hawthorn is not spiny like the hawthorn that grows in Europe and is usually not more than a metre high. The simple spiral leaves are broadly oval with slightly toothed margins. In spring the young leaves, reddish-coloured at first, open out with the flowers — pale pink or white, depending on the variety. The fruit is a pome like that of the apple but black in colour and not edible.

Two other shrubs which are in

bloom are Chinese Privet (*Ligustrum sinense*) and Bentham's Rosewood (*Dalbergia benthami*). Chinese Privet, an erect bush commonly grown in gardens as a hedge plant, is rarely seen in bloom because it is usually continuously cut back to keep it in shape. Growing wild, however, it is covered with small white flowers formed in dense panicles and giving out a strong scent like newly mown hay. The flowers are similar to the European Lilac having four joined petals, only two stamens and two carpels. The leaves are oval, growing in opposite pairs with entire margins. The fruit is a small, black berry.

Bentham's Rosewood is a sprawling, woody climber with alternate leaves divided into seven leaflets. The plant has inflorescences of small, white, pea-like flowers that are quite strongly perfumed. It is common on the road south of Tai Po.

A shrub or small tree with an edible, fragrant-smelling fruit that may also be seen along the road is the Guava (*Psidium guajava*). It has oval leaves borne in opposite pairs, forming two rows. The lateral veins of the leaf-blade are very prominent and numerous. In summer it bears white flowers very similar to Rose Myrtle (*Rhodomyrtus tomentosa*) formed in ones, twos or threes in the leaf axils. The fruit, which ripens at the end of July, is green at first, later turning yellow or pink according to the variety. The Guava is not native to Hong Kong, having been introduced from tropical America, but is now naturalised.

A curious shrub growing by the road is Hedge Sageretia (*Sageratia theezans*). Not a very attractive plant, its flowers are small and inconspicuous with parts in rings of five. Its leaves are simple, ovate, and alternate with large stem spines in their axils which protect the plant from browsing animals.

Although the vegetation along the roadside is rather sparse, with much bare ground on the left, quite a variety of herbaceous plants manage to survive. One of the most attractive of these is the Lavender Sorrel (*Oxalis corymbosa*), a low-growing, tufted plant with a bulbous rhizome. It has characteristic trifoliate leaves, each divided into three leaflets like the Shamrock, with small, attractive purplish-pink flowers borne in clusters on a flowering axis that comes out of the soil. It seems to flower over most of the year, and should be in bloom in March.

Seven members of the Daisy Family (Compositae) found along the road

Lavender Sorrel
Oxalis corymbosa

Tassel Flower
Emilia sonchifolia

include: White Bush Aster *(Aster baccharoides)*; Hairy Bur-Marigold *(Bidens pilosa)*; *Elephantopus tomentosa*; Tassel Flower *(Emilia sonchifolia)*; *Erigeron bonariensis*; *Gynura crepidioides*, and *Lactuca indica*. The Daisy Family is noted for producing compact flower-heads (capitula). The structure is often mistaken for a single flower but in reality is composed of many small flowers. The White Bush Aster is not blooming in March but the Hairy Bur-Marigold is. An annual with tripinnate leaves in opposite pairs and oval leaflets with ser-

rate margins, the plant's flower-heads have white ray florets with a yellow centre of disc florets, shaped like tiny bells. The fruit is black, with two or three barbed awns on top that catch onto animals' coats so the fruit can be dispersed.

Elephantopus tomentosa has alternate, simple ovate leaves with an undulating margin. They are very rough to the touch *(tomentosa* refers to this), especially on the under-surface, due to a dense covering of hairs. It does not flower in March. Tassel Flower is an annual with alternate, guitar-shaped, smooth leaves. The purplish-red flower-heads formed in pairs are shaped like a flask with a narrow neck while the florets are bell-like. The fruit has a parachute apparatus like that of the Dandelion for dispersal by wind. The Tassel Flower should not be confused with the Iron Plant whose flower-heads are purplish-blue in colour, more numerous and less flask-like in shape. The leaves of the Iron Plant are not guitar-shaped; they are oblong and softly hairy.

Erigeron bonariensis, common along the road, is a hairy annual with alternate, lance-shaped pointed leaves. The inflorescence is a dense panicle of small yellow flower-heads; the outer ray florets have very short corollas so that they do not stick out as in a Daisy. The fruit is flattened and crowned with many hairs to form a parachute apparatus for wind dispersal.

Gynura crepidioides is an annual with alternate ovate, pointed, simple leaves. The leaf margin is serrate and may be irregularly lobed. It can be seen flowering in March, with terminal clusters of orange-brown flower-heads which are elongate and tend to hang down as they get older. This species is recorded in the Chinese Flora and appears to be native to Hong Kong, although not listed in the *Hong Kong Check List* of plants. *Lactuca sativa* is the cultivated lettuce, so it is an escape from the vegetable gardens of the New Territories. When in bloom, it forms a branching inflorescence of yellow flower-heads.

When you reach the signpost saying 'Disused Mine', you will see tall spikes of the grass *Neyraudia reynaudiana* on both sides of a left turning. The grass is taller than a person, with conspicuous silver-grey tufts. Take this turning. The road directly ahead leads to the old mine, but you should turn into the rough road on your right. It winds in a gentle arc upwards. The road gives way to a hill path on the right. The gentle slope gradually becomes steeper. You are now passing through typical Hong Kong scrubland vegetation. Rose Myrtle and *Gordonia axillaris* are found here. *Rhaphiolepis indica* is also common, giving the hillside a touch of colour. The Hairy-fruited Abacus Plant *(Glochidion eriocarpum)* is exhibiting pinkish fruits. *Melastoma sanguineum* and *Eurya chinensis* are also seen but they are not flowering.

The trees found on this hillside are all stunted. Here and there you may see patches of a wild honeysuc-

Erigeron bonariensis

Lactuca sativa

kle in bloom. It is the Large-flowered Honeysuckle *(Lonicera macrantha)*, named for its showy golden flowers. The simple leaves are in pairs, with racemes of flowers in their axils. It is usually the first of Hong Kong's native species of Honeysuckle to flower in spring.

The path climbs up to the lowest peak of the Hunchbacks. Keep this peak at the western end of the range in sight as you climb up to make sure you don't lose your way, for the path is crossed by others. When you have climbed for about half an hour and are near the top of the path, you will have your first sight of flowering Rhododendrons.

The first to be seen is usually the so-called Red Azalea *(Rhododendron simsii)* (see photograph on p. 56), covered in orange-pink blooms. This shrub has a dense covering of simple, spirally arranged leaves. The leaves

and branches when young have rust-coloured hairs. The flowers have five sepals covered with silvery hairs, five petals joined at their bases, ten stamens with purple-red anthers and orange filaments and a single hairy ovary with a long style and knob-like stigma.

A little further up you will encounter Farrer's Rhododendron *(Rhododendron farrerae)* (see photograph on p. 56), leafless and mantled with bright pink flowers. Smaller than *R. simsii*, it thrives in high altitudes on bare hillsides, whereas *R. simsii* is commonly found at much lower elevation. This species is common all along the Hunchbacks and the slopes of Ma On Shan. Its flowers closely resemble those of *R. simsii* except for their colour.

From the first peak of the Hunchbacks, you must take the ridge path eastwards towards Ma On Shan. There are a number of crests and dells but in general you gradually climb higher. There are steep drops on either side, particularly on the north. On that side the slopes are wooded, but the south side is mainly grassland. The reason for this is probably climatic. In summer, the southern slopes are exposed to the south-west monsoon and the full heat of the sun, while the northern slopes are protected. In spring, particularly in March when the Rhododendrons are in bloom, there is mist on the northern face, but the southern slopes remain mist-free. The misty coolness of the northern face allows woodland to thrive despite the steepness of the land, although the trees are generally rather stunted.

Two species of oak (Quercus) are common here. Both have spiral, simple leaves and prominent, pointed axillary buds covered with brown scales. One species has thick, leathery leaves with a smooth margin and white under-surface, the other has larger and more elongate leaves with a toothed margin. Other trees of interest are Anneslea fragrans, Eriobotrya fragrans, Altingia chinensis and Ormosia emarginata.

Anneslea fragrans is a small evergreen tree with alternate, simple, rather leathery leaves of elongate shape. In March this tree produces umbrella-shaped groups of pink flowers at the tips of its branches. The flowers never open very wide, but look as if permanently in bud, and are rather waxy. Each has five joined, off-white fleshy sepals, red on the under-side, five joined petals, thirty stamens and a three-chambered ovary with a single style. The corolla can be removed in one piece and when folded out the petals look like a row of soldiers with pink heads and yellow bodies.

The Wild Loquat (Eriobotrya fragrans), also blooming in March, is clad in pale pink or white blossoms, like a miniature variety of apple blossom. An evergreen tree which can shoot up to 8 metres in height, it is only the size of a bush on the Hunchbacks. The leaves, simple and alternate, are toothed near the tip. Brown hairs cover the young leaves. Each flower has five furry, brown sepals, five notched petals and a mass of yellow stamens.

The Mountain Litchi (Altingia chinensis) bears small, inconspicuous flowers. The leaves are simple and spiral, with finely toothed edges. Both male and female flowers lack petals and are grouped into separate rounded heads occurring on the same tree. The fruit is brown and inedible, containing many three-sided winged seeds which the wind disperses. The tree normally grows to a height of 17 metres but on the Hunchbacks it is not more than 2 metres tall.

The Emarginate-leaved Ormosia (Ormosia emarginata) has alternate leaves pinnately divided, rather like those of the Ash tree. The leaflets are unusually shaped — notched at the apex ('emarginate'). The leaves are thick and leathery, a feature probably related to their exposed location. This species belongs to the Pea Family, and the white flowers, formed in summer, resemble the Sweet Pea. The fruit is a flattened pod with two scarlet seeds inside. The tree can grow up to 10 metres high, but is only the size of a large bush here.

The ridge path along the Hunchbacks is about 1,800 metres long from the lowest peak up to Ma On Shan. There are at least three minor peaks to scale before reaching Ma On Shan, more than 700 metres high. On one portion of the walk, you can look back at the hillside sloping down behind you for what seems an alarming distance. However, most of the ridge path is fairly safe as long as you are able to climb.

About half-way along the ridge path you will see Rhododendron westlandii (see photograph on p. 56), Hong Kong's largest flowered rhododendron. In March, blooms are formed in groups of five or six, light orchid-purple in colour with the upper petal spotted with orange. It is a beautiful flower with a strange but pleasant smell, somewhat like cinnamon. This plant has spiral, lance-shaped leaves and large, pointed axillary buds.

Rhododendron ovatum (see photograph on p. 56) is found at the beginning of the ridge walk and most of the way along the path, particularly on the northern side. This, too, produces attractive, strongly-scented pure white flowers, although they may be a light shade of pink at the time of opening, with purple spots on the upper petals. The plant may grow up to 3 metres high, with simple, spiral leaves. The young leaves, red in colour, come out with the flowers.

The only other Rhododendron you may see is R. simiarum, found on the northern face of the Hunchbacks, therefore difficult to reach. The flowers, rose-coloured when in bud, become lighter hued as they open, even perhaps turning white. The undersurface of its leaves is covered with white or corky-brown powder and the leaf margins curve downwards.

The reason most of our Rhododendron species only grow on mountains is probably because they occur normally in northerly climes and in Hong Kong they are on the southernmost limit of distribution. Hence the only place for them to survive is high up where it is cooler, and cloud mist often envelopes them. Like most mountain species, they tend to be small.

A tree of striking beauty that you are sure to see in March, when it is in bloom, is Symplocos decora Hance. It is an evergreen with alternate, rather leathery, simple leaves. The whole tree is covered in a mass of small white flowers, looking like a bridal bouquet. When the flowers first open they are a delicate shade of mauve, but the colour soon fades to white. They have a strong sweet perfume that attracts many insect visitors. Each flower has five joined sepals, five petals, twenty prominent stamens and a single ovary with a projecting style.

Towards the end of the ridge walk one leaves the trees and shrubs behind. Now the hillside is covered with grass only. In one place there is a patch of Sword Grass (Miscanthus floridulus) nearly as tall as a person on either side of the path, and an area of Bamboo. Hidden in the grass are some flowering herbs of the Daisy Family. The Hairy Gerbera (Gerbera piloselloides) stands out clearly with large white bud-like flower-heads occurring singly at the end of a long stalk. Another composite is Youngia japonica, which also has a rosette of leaves at ground level from the centre of which a flowering stem rises, terminating in groups of two or three yellow flower-heads. It is odd to find this plant so high up as it usually occurs at low levels on patches of waste ground.

At one point the grassy areas are almost entirely replaced by a curious low-growing shrub smelling strongly of mint. It is a species of Symplocos. The leaves are broadly ovate and alternate. This plant does not flower in March.

By the time you reach this area, you must prepare yourself for a long, steady climb up the last part of the ridge path to Ma On Shan. At the Peak, provided there is no mist, you have superb views of Tolo Harbour, Plover Cove Reservoir to the north, and Lion Rock to the south. To the north-east is Tolo Channel and Port Island and to the west Tai Mo Shan. Be very careful to follow the right path. There is a path to the left on the Hunchbacks that should be ignored on the way up. The way is perfectly obvious in clear weather because you have the peak of Ma On Shan before you as a guide, but in mist it is not so easy.

The downward route is steep at first. Quite soon you come to a point where there is a left turn going downwards. Ignore this and carry on straight ahead. The path will carry you over the crest of a hill and on over grassy hilltops until it eventually turns to the right and follows a long ridge down towards the disused mine.

The vegetation on the hilltops is mainly grass, but a few bushes of *Rhododendron farrerae* can still be seen, as well as two delicate flowering herbs: Wild Violet *(Viola diffusa)* and Skullcap *(Scutellaria indica)*. The Wild Violet is tufted and hairy, often putting out runners at the ends of which new plants form. The leaves are oval with margins of rounded teeth. The pale purple flowers are formed singly on long stalks and look like the cultivated Violet. The Skullcap is also very hairy and has opposite leaves with similar rounded teeth in the margin. It forms pale mauve flowers marked with dark mauve

streaks. These two little herbs delight the eye, for there are not many plants at this elevation.

The ridge path eventually becomes obscure in the region of the disused iron mine; a landslip has removed the lower part of it. However, you can follow the fringe of the landslip down until you come to a terrace. Turn right into this and make your way down to the road below. At one point there is a large area covered by the fern *Nephrolepis biserrata*. It propagates itself by forming slender runners that root and produce new frond-bearing stocks.

Having reached the road turn left and follow it through until it joins another road into which you should turn right. After a little while along this road you cross a bridge over a river. On the other side are a few houses which are part of Ma On Shan Tsuen. Follow the road through and you will find it becomes the one you started on at the beginning of the walk. Retrace your steps back to the ferry, thence to the Chinese University.

Nephrolepis biserrata frond

Red Azalea
Rhododendron simsii

Farrer's Rhododendron
Rhododendron farrerae

Westland's Rhododendron
Rhododendron westlandii

Oval-leaved Azalea
Rhododendron ovatum

Hong Kong Iris
Iris speculatrix

Wax Tree
Rhus succedanea

Mountain Orange
Melodinus suaveolens

Hilo Holly
Ardisia crenata Sims

57

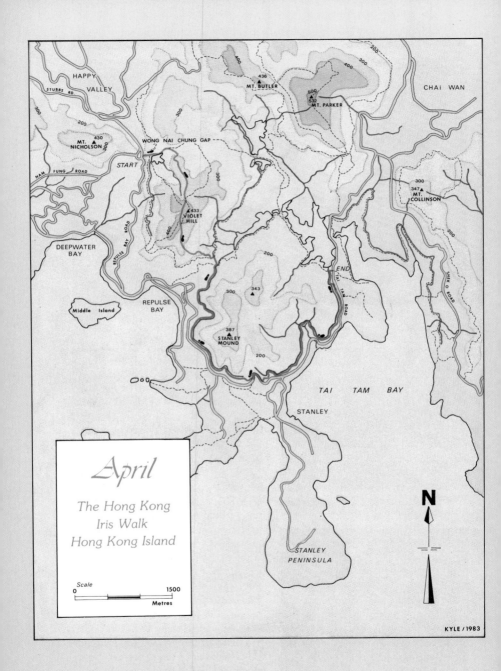

HAPPY
VALLEY
STUBBS RD.
MT.
NICHOLSON
430
NAM FUNG ROAD
START
WONG NAI CHUNG GAP
REPULSE BAY ROAD
VIOLET
HILL
433
DEEPWATER
BAY
Middle Island
REPULSE
BAY
MT. BUTLER
436
MT. PARKER
500
532
CHAI WAN
MT.
COLLINSON
347
300
END
TAI TAM ROAD
SHEK O ROAD
343
300
STANLEY
MOUND
387
200
200
TAI TAM BAY
STANLEY
STANLEY
PENINSULA

April

The Hong Kong
Iris Walk
Hong Kong Island

Scale
0   1500
Metres

N

KYLE / 1983

April

The Hong Kong Iris Walk
Wong Nai Chung Gap to
Tai Tam Tuk Reservoir via
Violet Hill and Stanley Mound
Time: 6 — 7 hours

The route in brief

Hong Kong's sole local species of Iris is to be found growing on grassy slopes on Hong Kong Island, between Repulse Bay and Shek O on the island's southern side. To see it, one has to trek along the spine of the island, to Violet Hill, along the water catchment of Tai Tam that goes around Stanley Mound above Repulse Bay and down a steep path to Stanley Gap Road, then on towards Red Hill and Tai Tam Harbour, descending into Tai Tam Road at the southern end of the Tai Tam Tuk Reservoir.

Travel along Wong Nai Chung Gap Road to a small garage just past the Hong Kong Cricket Club. Mount the stone steps leading up to a bridge over the road. At the top of the steps turn left and follow the approach road to the Tai Tam Country Park. About half a mile along this road you come to a crest. Take the ascending steps on your right that go to a path leading to Violet Hill. After passing through a bamboo thicket, fork right. The path crosses an upland valley, where the Hong Kong Iris is found, and climbs a hill. Half-way up fork left and follow this path round the side of the hill and down to a water catchment. Turn to the right here and follow the path on the right side of the water catchment, around Stanley Mound above Repulse Bay Road.

At length you will be above Stanley where the path comes to a dead end. Shortly before this take a steep path down to the Stanley Gap Road and turn left on to it. About 100 metres along the road mount the steps on your left leading to another water catchment. Turn right on to the path that follows the catchment towards Red Hill and Tai Tam Harbour. After descending some steps you will emerge on the Tai Tam Road at the southern end of the Tai Tam Tuk Reservoir. Here there are plenty of buses to take you home.

The Walk

This involves a fairly fierce uphill trek, then gently eases into a path which follows the water catchment area. If you started out in the morning, Violet Hill would be your natural stop for a picnic lunch. Here you can enjoy the view over Repulse Bay and the southern part of Hong Kong Island. As this is only about 1½ hours into the walk, it might mean an early lunch. The other possible stopping place is somewhere along the water catchment.

Along the approach road to the Tai Tam Country Park you may see the Fingerleaf Morning Glory (Ipomoea digitata). This flowers in summer, producing sprays of pink, cone-shaped flowers with dark throats and the petals white on the outside. Two other climbers are seen along the road. One is the Wild Kudzu Vine (Pueraria phaseoloides), a member of the Pea Family which flowers in summer. It has rather large, noticeable

Wild Kudzu Vine
Pueraria phaseoloides

tripinnate leaves. The whole plant is densely covered with rust-coloured hairs. The other climber is the Himalaya Creeper (Parthenocissus himalayana), which has similar leaves divided into three leaflets, with long leaf-stalks. The Himalaya Creeper climbs by means of tendrils, formed opposite the leaves, that have adhesive disc-like tips that hold on to any support. In autumn the leaves turn a vivid red before falling.

The road climbs through typical Hong Kong hill scrubland featuring such common shrubs as Eurya chinensis, Breynia fruticosa, the Hong Kong Hawthorn (Rhaphiolepis indica), and Rose Myrtle (Rhodomyrtus tomentosa), not quite in bloom. The curious spiny shrub Sageratia theezans is also present. Two other shrubs of interest are the Hilo Holly (Ardisia crenata Sims), and the Small Persimmon (Diospyros vaccinioides).

Hilo Holly (see photograph on p. 57), an evergreen found in the woodland's shady areas, grows to a height of about 1 metre. The spiral, simple, rather elongate leaves with wavy, scalloped edges, are thick and leathery. The leaf-stalks are dark purple. In June it produces clusters of purple-pink, star-like flowers and later bright red berries are formed.

The Small Persimmon is densely branched, about one metre tall, and with small, alternate, simple, pointed leaves in two rows on the stems. Small greenish flower buds open in May. The fruit, an edible, oval-shaped black berry, ripens in late summer.

Among the trees found along the road are White Popinac (Leucaena leucocephala), several of which are

Small Persimmon
Diospyros vaccinioides

now in bloom; specimens of the Round-leaved Litsea *(Litsea rotundifolia)*; and one or two specimens of the fairly rare Strawberry Tree *(Myrica rubra)*. Watch out for the Wild Mangosteen *(Garcinia oblongifolia)*, an attractive evergreen tree. It has opposite, simple, ovate leathery-textured leaves and flowers in May. The male flowers are yellow and appear in groups; the female are green and solitary, found on the same tree. The fruit is yellow when ripe. It is edible but can stain the teeth.

Another tree of interest is the Hog Plum *(Choerospondias axillaris)*, towering 20 metres high. It belongs to a family of trees which include the Rhus that can cause skin irritation. The leaves of the Hog Plum are divided and spirally arranged. There are five pairs of leaflets, plus a terminal one. In April there are panicles of small, purple-red flowers in the leaf axils and later small, yellow, egg-shaped fruits are formed. These are used in

wine-making and in Chinese medicine.

Among the few herbaceous plants growing at the side of the road are the Sword Grass *(Miscanthus floridulus)*, *Ageratum conyzoides*, *Bidens pilosa* as well as Wild Lettuce *(Lactuca indica)*, which produces an erect stem about 90 cm high that terminates in a panicle of yellow flowerheads.

After climbing up the road for a while you come to a crest with ascending steps on your right. They lead onto a hill path that takes you through scrubland towards Violet Hill. Take a narrow path of earthen steps directly ahead. The most common of the scrubland bush plants you see in this area are Hong Kong Heather *(Baeckea frutescens)*, *Eurya japonica*, Chinese New Year Flower *(Enkianthus quinqueflorus)*, *Gordonia axillaris* and *Melastoma sanguineum*, none of which is flowering in April. The Hong Kong Hawthorn, however, may still be in bloom although it may no longer be seen at

Eurya japonica

61

its best. Just beginning to flower is the *Gardenia jasminoides* whose large fragrant white blooms gradually change to creamy yellow during the one day that the flower is open. This Gardenia is the wild ancestor of the cultivated double gardenia.

An interesting shrub is the Japanese Supple-jack *(Berchemia racemosa)*. It is a straggly plant, the branches often overhanging other shrubs. Its leaves are simple, ovate and alternate with pointed tips. At this time of year the ends of the branches bear attractive sprays of elongate red drupes (a fruit like that of the cherry). Occurring here and there along the path is *Pentaphylax euryoides*, a shrub not often found in Hong Kong. It has alternate, simple leaves of a broadly oval shape. Under ideal conditions it can attain a height of 10 metres, but on the dry and exposed hillside it reaches a height of only 2 metres.

Few of the trees seen here are more than 2 to 3 metres high; they look more like large shrubs. The Chinese Red Pine *(Pinus massoniana)* is quite common. Some of the trees look unhealthy, as if dying from a disease. When healthy they show fresh, bright green shoots.

Also seen here are the Ivy Tree *(Schefflera octophylla), Abarema lucida, Machilus thunbergii,* all of which also grow in the forest on the slopes of Tai Mo Shan, and *Rhus succedanea.* Like Hong Kong's two other common local species of Sumac, *Rhus succedanea* (see photograph on p. 57) has once-pinnate leaves arranged spirally. New leaves open out in April, looking reddish, particularly on the under-surface. The leaf-stalks too are red. By contrast *Rhus hypoleuca* has a white under-surface and *Rhus chinensis* has characteristic green flanges on either side of the midrib. *R. succedanea* flowers in April, producing clusters of tiny greenish-yellow flowers.

Another small woodland tree is *Alangium chinense* which can attain a height of about 5 metres, but here reaches only half this height. It has alternate simple leaves, ovate with a pointed tip. It flowers in May. *Homalium cochinchinensis* grows on the hillside. In March when it blooms, it is covered with tassels of small white flowers. It appears that this area is regenerating woodland from scrubland as both types of plants occur mixed together but the woodland species are not tall enough to be called trees. Typical small trees of scrubland found along the path are *Ilex asprella, Rhus hypoleuca, Ficus variolosa* and *Litsea rotundifolia.* Per-

Pentaphylax euryoides

Alangium chinense

haps as time passes the tree species will grow larger and push out these scrubland species.

As you follow the path up the hillside you will notice several kinds of climbing plants. One of these is the common *Gnetum montana* characterised by stout, trailing branches bearing ovate, leathery leaves in opposite pairs. The stems twist round any suitable support. In April *G. montana* shows elongate cone-like structures in groups at the branch tips. These are either female, in which case there is a series of ovules in rings one above the other, or male, where there are rings of stamens similarly arranged. Later the seeds of the female cones become covered by an orange fleshy bract to form a sort of fruit. This plant is rather a curiosity, having hardly any other close relatives in the world. It is a Gymnosperm, a plant which has naked seeds, not enclosed inside a carpel as in the flowering plants.

Another climber found here is *Mil-*

lettia speciosa, a close relative of *M. nitida*. A tall woody plant, it has alternate, once-pinnate leaves which when young are coated with dense white hairs. It is the most showy of all our *Millettia* species when in bloom in August, producing large pea-like creamy flowers. There is a green spot in the middle of the large standard petal at the back of the flower to attract bees. The root of this plant is much sought after by local villagers as a cure for various ailments such as low back pain, rheumatism and a dry cough.

The common climbing plant genus *Smilax* is represented on Violet Hill by *S. corbularia*, which has elongate leaves, and *S. glauca* which has shorter leaves. The climbing fern *Lygodium japonicum* also occurs frequently. The only other ferns to be seen are False Staghorn Fern *(Dicranopteris linearis)* and *Blechnum orientale*. The latter forms large clumps in open places along the path.

The path goes through a bamboo thicket for a short distance and then forks. Take the path on your right. Here in an upland valley surrounded on three sides by hills, you will find the Hong Kong Iris *(Iris speculatrix)* (see photograph on p. 57). A delicate perennial, it is the only local species of Iris, appearing mainly on Hong Kong Island. Usually growing among grass, you will have to look hard to find it as it is no more than 30 cm high. The rhizome gives rise to grass-like leaves about 15-20 cms long that taper to a point. It commences flowering towards the end of March and may still be out to the end of April. It produces no more than two flowers on one stem, one terminal and the second one borne below, but they are not open at the same time.

Each flower has six outer petal-like segments the colour of pale purple. The outer whorl of three, called falls, hang downwards as a landing stage for insects; the inner whorl of three stand upwards in the flower's centre to form the rises to attract insects.

Insects, bringing pollen from another flower, seek the nectary at the base of the tube formed by the united petal-like segments. As the insect goes in, it pushes back a flap on the petal-like style exposing the stigmatic surface on which pollen is deposited. When the insect penetrates deeper into the flower, pollen rubs on to it from the anther above. As the insect backs out, having had its fill of nectar, it closes the flap over the stigmatic surface, thus preventing self-pollination in the plant. If you examine the falls you will see that they are intricately marked with purple lines that lead into the flower. There is a central orange ridge (leading from a cream-coloured area) forming a raised track along which the insect walks to reach the nectar. All these markings serve as guides to lead the insect into the flower for cross-pollination.

upland valley towards a hill. About halfway up there is a path to the left leading round the side of the hill and down towards the water catchment. Follow this. The descent is steep, going through scrubland. *Gordonia axillaris* and *Baeckea frutescens* are the most common shrubs. Great clumps of Black Sedge *(Ghania tris-*

tis) are also common and you should be able to spot the Wild Honeysuckle *(Lonicera japonica)* in flower.

A small tree quite common in this area is *Itea chinensis* which, in late March or early April, is covered by much-branched inflorescences of small white flowers standing up like Christmas tree candles.

The descent from Violet Hill brings you to the Tai Tam Intermediate Reservoir where there is a water catchment. Turn to the right when you meet it and follow the path on the right bank round the wooded slopes of Stanley Mound. The walk is pleasant, rimmed by trees. There are a number of Wood-oil Trees *(Aleurites montana)*, which should be covered with white flowers in April. The male trees are distinguished by the flowers' yellow stamens, the female by the green ovaries. White Popinac *(Leucaena leucocephala)*, seen at the beginning of the walk, is also represented here. This, too, will be in flower, sporting globe-shaped groups of small, creamy blossoms and twice-divided, lacy leaves.

Further along the water catchment path are trees of Prickly Ash *(Zanthoxylum avicennae)*, recognised by its spirally arranged, once-pinnate leaves with unpleasant prickles along the midrib. There are about eleven or twelve almost opposite pairs of leaflets plus one terminal one. The trunk has a toothed bark. Later in the year panicles of small greenish flowers are formed, followed by purplish-red berries. A common woodland tree, usually small in Hong Kong, it should not be confused with the true Ash (species of *Fraxinus*). The

Chinese Ash *(Fraxinus retusa)*, the only locally recorded species, is present along the water catchment path. The leaves usually have five leaflets. It forms terminal inflorescences in March, made up of many small white flowers. The fruit develops a wing which helps dispersal by the wind.

Rhus succedanea, encountered on Violet Hill, also grows along the water catchment area. One may confuse it with the Ash trees because its leaves are also once-pinnate, but the leaflets always droop downwards from the midrib at an angle, whereas in *Frax-* *inus retusa* and *Zanthoxylum avicennae* the leaflets are in one plane with the midrib.

Other typical forest trees along this path are the Ivy Tree *(Schefflera octophylla)*, *Acronychia pedunculata* and the Smooth-barked Mempat *(Cratoxylum ligustrinum)*. The flowers of the Mempat resemble those of the European Japonica *(Cydonia japonica)*. They are small and orange-red, coming out in April, and should not be missed.

Three trees flowering in April are *Pentaphylax euryoides, Tricalysia*

Smooth-barked Mempat
Cratoxylon ligustrinum

dubia and the Fragrant Snow-bell *(Styrax odoratissimus). P. euryoides* was seen earlier on Violet Hill but along the water catchment area it grows larger, probably because here it is more sheltered. In the axils of the leaves towards the ends of the branches are brown spikes made up of many tiny flower buds which open to form small white fragrant flowers with their parts in whorls of five.

Tricalysia dubia is a small, evergreen tree with opposite, sharp-pointed oblong leaves. Flower buds appear in groups on short stalks in the leaf axils. They are white when open, with the parts in whorls of four. The ovary has two carpels and the fruit is a small red berry.

The Fragrant Snow-bell, which attains a height of 10 metres, has alternate, simple oval leaves. The white, fragrant flowers develop singly or in twos or threes in the leaf axils towards the ends of the shoots. The fruit is pointed at one end and covered with star-like scales.

As you follow the contours of Stanley Mound, you may see some bright carmine fruits much like the European Sycamore in shape, with two joined nut-like portions from each of which arises a wide-angled wing. One-seeded fruits of this type, with hard dry walls drawn out into a wing for wind dispersal, are known as samaras. As this has two wings it is a double samara. When the fruit is ripe the two halves split apart and either gyrate slowly to the ground or are carried away by the wind. This remarkable fruit belongs to the Long-leaved Maple *(Acer laevigatum)*, one of our four local species of Maple

Tricalysia dubia

66

Fragrant Snow-bell
Styrax odoratissimus

common on Hong Kong Island. It is a woodland species.

On this contour path you are on the fringe of the forest that covers the slopes of Stanley Mound. Below the path is Repulse Bay Road. This is a transitional zone between forest and hill scrubland. The Mountain Orange *(Melodinus suaveolens)* (see photograph on p. 57) which can become a high climber occurs in many places and the trees are festooned with white flowers in dense clusters, exuding a strong perfume. One or two of the large orange-like fruits left over from the previous year may be seen.

The water catchment path eventually comes to a dead end. You are now above Stanley Gap Road and opposite the Stanley Peninsula, commanding excellent views. Walk down a steep path to the main road below,

then turn left and follow the road in the direction of the Stanley turn-off for about 100 metres. Look out for some steps on your left. Take these and then turn right on reaching a water catchment path and proceed in the direction of Red Hill and Tai Tam Harbour, following the contours of Stone Hill. You are still on the fringe of forest and many of the trees seen earlier will be seen again.

At the southern end of Tai Tam Tuk reservoir steps lead down to the road. These will take you to the point where Tai Tam Reservoir Road crosses Tai Tam Road. There are plenty of buses to be taken from here to get you home. If you are very energetic, you may return via the Tai Tam Reservoir Road to where you started from at Wong Nai Chung Gap. But be warned: the journey is all uphill!

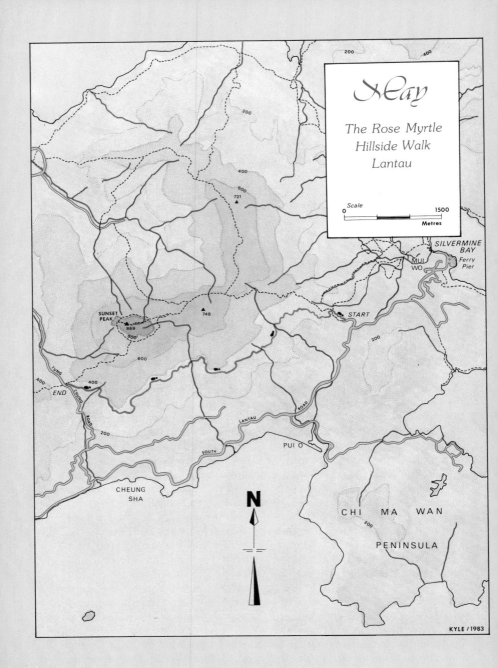

Map

The Rose Myrtle
Hillside Walk
Lantau

Scale

0   1500
                     Metres

SILVERMINE
BAY
MUI   Ferry
WO   Pier

200

START

200

721

SUNSET
PEAK
869

748

600

TUNG   600

END   CHUNG

400

400

200

ROAD

LANTAU   ROAD

SOUTH

PUI O

CHEUNG
SHA

N

CHI   MA   WAN

200

PENINSULA

KYLE / 1983

May

The Rose Myrtle Hillside Walk
Lantau
Time: 4 hours

The route in brief

R ose Myrtle *(Rhodomyrtus tomentosa)* is a common hillside
shrub which grows in great abundance on the mountainous slopes of
the big island of Tai Yue Shan or
Lantau.

To enjoy the walk, make an early
start. Board the ferry for Silvermine
Bay from the Outlying Districts Ferry
Pier in Central. Once in Silvermine
Bay, catch a bus for Pui O. Get off
at Nam Shan at the top of a hill half-
way to Pui O. About 50 metres further up, take the road turning right
from the main road. After a short
distance take a path on your right
through woodland and follow it past
a helipad to a meeting of four ways
where you turn left. Almost at once
there is another crossroads of paths.
Turn right on to the path leading upwards. Follow this up through woodland. It soon becomes a contour path
along the mid-levels of Sunset Peak.
You hug the hillside, winding in and
out and crossing a number of mountain streams before reaching Tung
Chung Pass Road. From here you
can board a bus back to Silvermine
Bay.

The Walk

This is a pleasant walk through the woodlands and hills of Hong Kong's biggest and, so far, most unspoiled island, overlooking many scenic sea- and mountain-scapes. Fairly early in your walk, you come to an authorised picnic site with tables and barbecue places already set out. However, as you will be passing through lovely grassy countryside, you can choose to stop where you will.

The trees at the beginning of the walk consist mainly of Brisbane Box *(Tristania conferta)* and Acacia *(Acacia confusa)*, both introduced trees in the woodlands. The Brisbane Box should be flowering, and the Acacia will be forming fruits. Brisbane Box (see photograph on p. 76) reaches a height of about 7 metres in Hong Kong, but grows much taller in its homeland, Australia. It has a reddish bark, and simple oval leaves pointed at both ends. The flowers are white, in small clusters borne in the leaf axils on a short flowering stem, and are somewhat hidden by the leaves. Each flower has five green pointed sepals joined at the base and five free petals with fringed edges. There are five bundles of stamens, each joined together by their filaments, opposite the petals. The stamens are very prominent and give the flower a frilly look.

Acacia confusa, a native of Taiwan and the Philippines, is a bushy tree about 7 metres high. The apparent leaves are simple. Actually, these structures are phyllodes, which are flattened leaf-stalks. The yellow flowers are tiny, in dense groups forming pom-poms, and are replaced by flattened pods.

The Chinese Red Pine *(Pinus massoniana)*, also seen at the beginning of the walk, is Hong Kong's only native pine. *Pinus elliottii*, which has longer needles than the native species, has been planted with great success in Hong Kong and is better at standing up to hill fires than the Chinese Red Pine. Pine trees form male and female cones on the same tree and new ones may be seen opening out in April. After shedding their pollen, the small male cones die, but the female cones take two and a half years to complete their development before the winged seeds are shed.

Climb a small hill through the woodland and you will come to a helipad used by the Army. The path soon descends to a point where there is a meeting of four ways. Take the left turning. Another few metres on, four paths meet again. This time, take the path on the right that leads upwards (the next one to it on the left leads downwards). There is a signpost to the Tung Chung Pass. You now have a 6½-kilometre walk before joining the main road across the island to Tung Chung.

The path climbs gently upwards among *Casuarina* trees, also known as the She-oak, Horsetail Tree and Iron-wood because the wood is very hard. It is a member of the Family Casuarinaceae. The one found here, *C. equisetifolia*, has been introduced from the Pacific Islands and Southeast Asia. In the full tropics, it can be a very tall tree, but here it is not usually more than 10 metres in height. It is salt-resistant and grows

Iron-wood *or* Horsetail Tree
Casuarina equisetifolia

well on sandy shores, where it is often planted.

The She-oak looks remarkably like a pine tree, but closer examination reveals that the apparent needle leaves are actually branches. The branches themselves are borne in rings, rather like those of the Horsetail (species of *Equisetum*). The leaves are reduced to scales to minimise loss of water vapour, an adaptation to the dry, exposed habitat where the tree is normally found. The She-oak may bloom in May, bearing both male and female flowers in catkin-like groups. Male flowers consist of a single stamen and the female ones of two carpels. When ripe, the female catkins resemble small cones. They contain tiny fruits that are nut-like and winged, and partly enclosed by a woody sheath.

After about half an hour, you come to a pleasant spot where there are picnic tables. Brisbane Box provides good shade and there is an excellent view of the coast beyond Pui O and the Chi Ma Wan peninsula.

Here you will see the Rose Myrtle everywhere (see photograph on p. 76). This is one of the most common of Hong Kong's native hillside shrubs. The flowers, deep rose pink in colour, gradually fade almost to white in one or two days. The leaves are simple and arranged in opposite pairs. Like the Brisbane Box, it is a member of the Myrtle Family (Myrtaceae). The fruits are filled with seeds. Commonly known as *Kong Nim* (dark red memories) or Barley Bues, the fruit ripens in September. It has a raspberry red pulp and is quite tasty. It can be made into a jelly preserve.

Covering much of the exposed hillsides is False Staghorn Fern *(Dicranopteris linearis)*. A common Hong Kong fern, it has leaves that fork into equal halves at least two or three times. The ultimate branches are leafy; they bear numerous lobes that are joined at their base. Scattered here and there at the side of the path are Oriental Blechnum *(Blechnum orientale)*, Bracken Fern *(Pteridium aquilinum)* and the Climbing Fern *(Lygodium japonicum)*. *B. orientale*

Bracken Fern
Pteridium aquilinum

has rosettes of large compound leaves, once-pinnate with a single row of closely spaced, oblique, pointed leaflets. The sori are continuous along both sides of the leaflet mid-vein on the under-side, protected by a flap opening towards the vein. The Climbing Fern twists round any suitable support. The leaf midribs show indefinite growth and bear forked pinnae inserted singly. Each fork has four to five leaflets that may be subdivided again into two or three. The ultimate leaflets are variably lobed, usually from three to seven, with the middle one much longer than the side ones.

Small delicate plants that thrive in damp, shady places and along streams include the fern *Sphenomeris chinensis*. Its fronds droop down and are very dissected. They are usually tripinnate and the ultimate segments are wedge-shaped. Other shade-loving plants include *Selaginella limbata*, a low-growing herb with unequally forking branches covered with small leaves of two sizes. There is a row of larger leaves on either side of the stem, and two rows of tiny, scale-like leaves are visible through a hand lens on the upper side of the stem. Rooting structures called rhizophores arise at the branch points. There are twelve species of *Selaginella* recorded in Hong Kong.

Further along the path, you leave the woodland behind and the hillside becomes scrubland. In exposed places, Rose Myrtle is replaced by grassland. You cross a number of streams and their waterfalls are delightful, especially after heavy rainfall.

Many interesting plants can be

Sphenomeris chinensis

seen along the wayside. Scattered here and there is the common Lantana *(Lantana camara)* and Buddha's Lamp *(Mussaenda pubescens)*. The Lantana was introduced into Hong Kong from tropical America and has rapidly naturalised itself. This shrub sometimes forms impenetrable thickets. Hairy, with a strong aromatic smell, it is characterised by its yellow, orange and pink flowers (changing colour in that order) occurring in dense heads at the ends of branches or in the leaf axils. The leaves are in opposite pairs, oval- to heart-shaped with a finely toothed margin. The fruit is a fleshy black drupe whose seeds are spread by birds.

Buddha's Lamp is a shrub growing up to 1.5 metres high, often putting out long climbing branches. The leaves, borne in opposite pairs, are oval with entire margins. From April onwards golden yellow unisexual flowers are formed in dense cymose clusters at the tip of the branches. Some of the flowers have one greatly

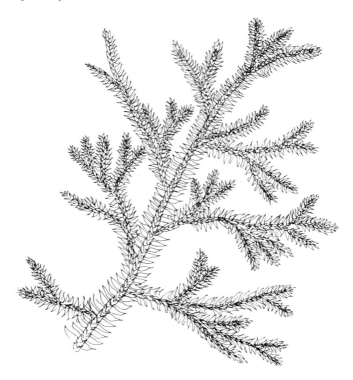

enlarged white sepal, looking like a pointed oval leaf, to attract insects. Its common name, Buddha's Lamp, may come from the way the white sepal looks like an old-fashioned oil lamp, the yellow flower at one end being the flame. The fruit is an oval, black capsule containing many minute seeds.

Other interesting plants seen along the wayside are two species of raspberry: *Rubus reflexus* and *Rubus parvifolius*. *R. reflexus* is a sprawling climber with stems covered by rust-coloured hairs, and has simple, five-lobed leaves which show attractive red and green markings when young. *R. parvifolius* shows no hairs, but has compound leaves made up of three leaflets that are white underneath. Both species are prickly and flower from May onwards. The flowers are white and inconspicuous, but later a small orange-red fruit is formed resembling the cultivated raspberry. It is edible and just as delicious.

A robust perennial herb frequently seen along the path is the Iron-weed *(Vernonia cinerea)*, with grey hairy stems. The lower leaves are alternate, hairy and oval-shaped with pointed tips and finely toothed margins; the upper leaves gradually become smaller and narrower. When it flowers, it produces a fairly dense panicle of bluish-purple flower-heads. The fruit is an achene, with white hairs for wind disperal.

An introduced species of *Clerodendrum* is common at the beginning of the hillside path. This is *C. viscosum* (see photograph on p. 76) which can grow to a height of more than two metres. It has broad but pointed simple leaves, soft and velvety to the touch. The inflorescence includes a number of flower-heads, each with ten white flowers in a cymose group. The end flower opens first and those below it open later. The flowers have five fused, velvety sepals and five joined petals. The petals soon fall, but the pale green sepals persist into the fruiting stage.

Here and there on the route is one of the five local species of Honeysuckle, appropriately called Gold and Silver Flower (*Lonicera japonica*) (see photograph on p. 76). When the flowers first open, they are almost white, but later change to cream and finally gold-yellow. The leaves are simple, arranged in pairs. The flowers are in groups of four in the leaf axils. The petals of the flower are elongate and fused with nectar-secreting glands (nectaries) at the base of the corolla tube. Only long-tongued insects such as butterflies and moths can reach the nectar. Since the pale flowers show up best at night and are most fragrant at this time, they are probably pollinated by moths. This honeysuckle climbs by means of its twisting stem.

A member of the Pea Family called the Tea Gourd (*Pteroloma triquetrum*) is found at the side of the path in several places. It has spikes of pinkish flowers, like those of the Sweet Pea, and is about 60 cms in height. The leaf stalks have characteristic flanges and the lamina is elongate and pointed. At the point where the leaf joins the stem is a pair of wing-like stipules.

There are excellent views of Cheung Sha (Long Beach) on a clear day and the sea looks most inviting, but it is a long way down. Towards the end of the contour path, you pass through pine woods. The road to Tung Chung can be seen below, but the path hugs the hillside and it takes some time to reach the road. There is a bus stop on the road near the junction with the path, and you can go back to Silvermine Bay. If it is getting late, you should walk down this road to the main coastal road from Ngong Ping where buses pass more frequently.

Rose Myrtle
Rhodomyrtus tomentosa

Brisbane Box
Tristania conferta

Clerodendrum viscosum

Wild Honeysuckle
Lonicera japonica

Parasol Mushroom
Lepiota species

Clavaria vermicularis

Chinese Lily
Lilium brownii

Caesalpinnia crista

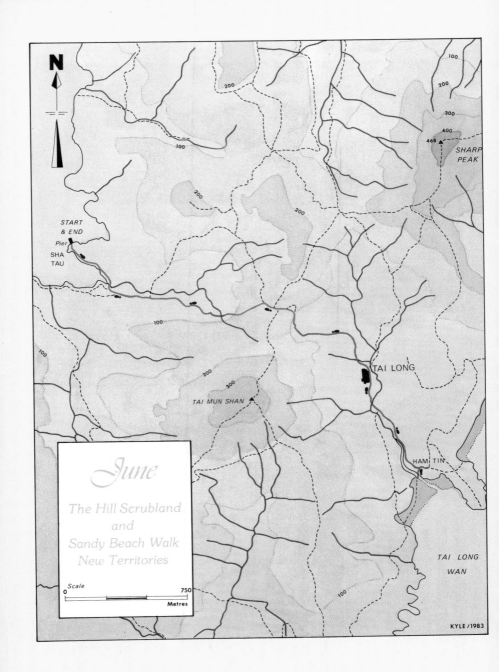

N

START
& END
Pier
SHA
TAU

SHARP
PEAK

468

TAI LONG

TAI MUN SHAN

HAM TIN

June

The Hill Scrubland
and
Sandy Beach Walk
New Territories

TAI LONG
WAN

Scale
0   750
Metres

KYLE/1983

June

The Hill Scrubland and Sandy
Beach Walk
Chek Keng to Tai Long Wan,
New Territories
Time: 4 — 5 hours

The route in brief

This walk takes you across hill scrubland to the beautiful beaches of Tai Long Wan where unusual salt- and sand-loving plants may be seen, for example St John's Lily and Cocklebur.

You start with a ferry ride across Tolo Harbour in the early morning to the bay of Tai Long in the northeastern part of the New Territories. You will be rewarded by excellent views of Ma On Shan, Nine Fathoms Cove and the Plover Cove Dam. You stop at a fishing village on Tap Mun Island and Kau Lau Wan where you can see floating rafts used for fish culture. The surrounding hills, attractive seascapes and traditional junks seen through floating mist appear almost like a Chinese painting.

Travel by bus or car to the Chinese University of Hong Kong and from there take the ferry to Chek Keng. After stops at Tap Mun Island and Kau Lau Wan you will reach Chek Keng — a journey of about 1 ½ hours. On landing turn right on to a cement path and follow it along the water's edge of Long Harbour. The path turns inland and crosses a bridge over a stream. On the far side of the bridge turn left and follow the path up to a T-junction where you turn left. The path continues upwards through a valley to a gap in the hills, after which it descends rapidly to the village of Tai Long. Take a right turn in the village opposite a cafe and follow a path in front of some houses. After a shrub-lined glade the path follows the banks of a tidal stream to an area of woodland. After the wood it soon reaches the beach by another cafe. The return route is the same, but in reverse. The ferry back to the Chinese University leaves from Chek Keng and you should allow at least two hours for the walk back in order to catch it.

The Walk

At Chek Keng you will see a cement path leading to the right from the jetty. Above this path is a bank covered with interesting plants from mixed habitats. Forest trees such as the Tallow-tree *(Sapium sebiferum)* and *Mallotus apelta* grow alongside seashore species like the Screw Pine *(Pandanus tectorius)* and Hong Kong Coconut *(Cerbera manghas)* or Sea Mango.

The Tallow-tree grows to about 7 metres and has alternate diamond-shaped leaves with long leaf-stalks. There are two small glands where the stalk joins the leaf-blade. The inflorescences, formed in summer, stick up from the ends of the branches like Christmas tree candles, the male flowers occurring in the upper part of the spike and the female in the lower. The fruit is a green globose capsule. The white seeds produce a fatty substance used in China for making candles.

The leaves of *Mallotus apelta* are shaped like spades in a pack of playing cards and have a white undersurface which flashes brightly when shaken by the wind. In June pendulous catkin-like racemes of tiny greenish flowers, either male or female, are produced. When the ovaries of the female flowers develop into fruits, they become covered by soft horn-like processes giving them a fuzzy look.

The Hong Kong Coconut also flowers in June. It has elongate simple leaves arranged spirally and crowded together at the ends of the branches. When the leaf is damaged, it exudes a milky-white poisonous juice which circulates throughout the tree. The fragrant flowers occur in loose terminal clusters and are white with a red centre. The pendulous fruit, at first green in colour, looks rather like a mango — hence it is also known as Sea Mango. Later, it becomes red and finally brown. The fruits fall into the sea and are dispersed by water, which is why the tree always grows along the shoreline. The fruits, washed onto the shore, dry out and look like small coconuts, hence the other common name, Hong Kong Coconut.

The Screw Pine, common throughout the Pacific region, is usually found along the shoreline forming impenetrable thickets. It is a spiny plant with a twisted trunk and an arrangement of leaves that follows this spiral pattern. The leaves resemble the elongated leaves of a pineapple plant. The large composite fruit formed by the ovaries of many flowers fused together, turns orange when ripe and looks like a pineapple. The pulpy tissue is edible. In summer, male or female flowers occur in terminal clusters on separate plants. The male inflorescence, conspicuous by the white bracts that protect it, gives out a strong perfume to attract butterflies and flies.

Proceeding along the cement path, you will see to your right the innermost part of Long Harbour which looks almost like an inland sea, landlocked on three sides. There are a few bushes of *Kandelia candel* in the inter-tidal zone which are almost submerged in water when the tide is in. At the high tide line and above are some small trees of another mangrove plant, the Milky Mangrove (*Excoecaria agallocha*). The whole plant contains a poisonous milky latex. Bend a leaf until it snaps and the white latex will ooze out. In June female plants are covered with brown three-lobed fruits. As these dry, they burst noisily and set the seeds free. Another mangrove plant along the shoreline is False Jasmine (*Clerodendrum inerme*), whose white tubular flowers seen in June resemble those of Jasmine. It forms an untidy sprawling bush.

Soon the cement path leaves the water's edge and passes through some flat land. Here is a typical seashore plant — *Vitex rotundifolia* — with blue-grey foliage. This creeping plant has oval, simple leaves arranged in opposite pairs. If the leaves or stems are crushed, they give off a pleasant aromatic smell. In June the plant bears pale, mauvey-blue flowers. The fruit is a globular capsule.

This area of flat, grassy land is host to the Parasol Mushroom (*Lepiota* species). When fully expanded (see photograph on p. 77), its cap

False Jasmine
Clerodendrum inerme

may be as much as 20 cms across in some species, e.g. *L. procera*. The cap is fawn-coloured with creamy white gills. Further along the path is a small fungus, *Clavaria vermicularis* (see photograph on p. 77), noticeable because of its bright orange forking branches.

The path soon takes you to a bridge over a stream, on your right. Cross the bridge and turn to the left, following the cement path parallel with the stream. Clumps of *Clerodendrum inerme* bloom along the bank. In this area of abandoned rice paddies are small trees conspicuously covered with clusters of red, pea-sized fruits which become black when fully ripe and are edible. This tree is the Sweet Viburnum *(Viburnum odoratissimum)* which has leathery, round leaves with a slight indentation at the tip arranged in opposite pairs.

The cement path begins to climb upwards through an area of False Staghorn Fern *(Dicranopteris linearis)* and some Chinese Red Pines. At the top of some steps you will come to a T-junction. Take the left turn and continue upwards on the cement path. You will observe a creeper, *Melothria heterophylla*, with three-lobed leaves (with tendrils borne opposite the leaf stalks) like those of the ivy. This plant is noted for its bright red fruit (green at first, then yellow) formed singly in the leaf axils. The fruits are delicate and apt to burst if you touch them. They are edible but not particularly tasty.

The path climbs steadily upwards through a valley. The hills on either side are covered with small shrubs not more than two metres high. Probably the most common are Rose Myrtle *(Rhodomyrtus tomentosa)* still in bloom, *Phyllanthus emblica* with green gooseberry-like fruits, *Helicteres angustifolia* and Wild Coffee *(Psychotria rubra)* both in bloom, *Melastoma candidum* and the Hairy-fruited Abacus Plant *(Glochidion eriocarpum)*, which is flowering and fruiting at the same time. The small yellow flowers hang like bells beneath the branches and the pink fruits with coral-red seeds inside, seen when the fruits burst open, are very conspicuous. *Embelia laeta* is noticeable because of the sprays of dark red fruits at ground level.

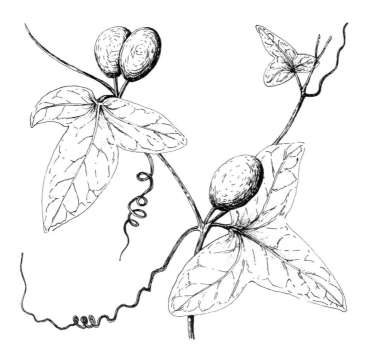

Melothria heterophylla

83

There are three very spiny shrubs of interest. These are *Sageratia theezans, Paliurus ramosissimus*, and *Fortunella hindsii*. *P. ramosissimus* has two sharp spines at the base of the leaf stalk that are equivalent to stipules, while *F. hindsii* has one spine in the axil of the leaf which is equivalent to a stem.

A pretty flowering shrub is *Symplocos panaliculata*. The tiny creamy flowers in terminal racemes cover the bush with a white mantle. The alternate leaves are oval-shaped with finely toothed edges.

If you are feeling hungry as you trudge up the hill, look out for the Wild Raspberry *(Rubus reflexus)* which should be laden with delicious fruit by now. This prickly, sprawling plant has palmately-lobed leaves often with attractive dark-red patterns. Another *Rubus* species is *R. parvifolius* but it is not yet fruiting. This has trifoliate leaves arranged spirally.

A few herbs manage to survive in this scrubland. Perhaps the most striking of these is Dog's Tail Bean *(Uraria macrostachya)* with its pagoda-like spike of purplish-pink, pealike flowers. The flowers occur in pairs in the axil of a pinkish-mauve bract. The whole plant is very hairy and prickly. It has alternate, once-pinnate leaves, usually with three pairs of leaflets plus one terminal one. The large standard petal at the back of the flower is a deep shade of purple spotted with yellow; the rest of the petals are a paler shade. The fruit is a pod.

Hong Kong's only species of lily, *Lilium brownii* (see photograph on p. 77), is another herbaceous plant that is flowering. It has a long stem bearing numerous alternate, narrow pointed leaves. At the top of the stem are one or two, rarely more, large white flowers. The six petals in two whorls are streaked purplish-brown on the outside, and the six stamens have reddish-brown anthers. This Chinese Lily perennates (lasts from one winter to the next) by means of an underground bulb. During the Japanese occupation of Hong Kong villagers survived a food shortage by eating lily bulbs.

Hedyotis uncinella is a herb with square stems and noticeable for the globular heads of tiny white flowers interspersed with mauve. Two large leafy bracts as well as two small ones are beneath the heads. Lower down the stem, in the axils of paired leaves, are bunches of small flowers.

The path climbs the valley to a gap in the hills. Chek Keng is now out of sight. The cement path descends quite rapidly and in the dis-

Mountain Kumquat
Fortunella hindsii

tance you will see the sea and the southern end of Tai Long Wan and small islands in the bay.

You are now going through hill scrubland with much the same type of plants you have already seen in the walk. Compare the three common species of *Rhus* which are present here. They all have once-pinnate alternate leaves with up to eight pairs of leaflets plus one terminal one. *Rhus hypoleuca* has large leaves with eleven to seventeen leaflets arranged in one plane, showing white underneath. The midrib is not winged. Creamy flowers are produced in September. *Rhus succedanea* has small leaves with seven to thirteen leaflets not all in one plane. They are drooping and are yellow-green underneath. The midrib is not winged and greenish flowers are produced in April. *Rhus chinensis* has large leaves with seven to thirteen leaflets arranged in one plane and yellowish underneath. The midrib is winged and creamy flowers come out in September. All three species produce sap that irritates the skin; this is cured by rubbing the affected area with the leaves of the Hairy-fruited Abacus (*Glochidion eriocarpum*) which, fortunately, grows nearby.

On the way down to Tai Long Wan, you will come across the golden-yellow flowers of *Desmos cochinchinensis*. They hang singly beneath the branches like bells, at first green then changing to yellow. They are very odd flowers as, at first sight, there appear to be no stamens and no ovary in the centre. This is because the lower part of the petals arch over them. If you gently pull on the petals,

a triangular area of densely packed stamens may be seen, surrounding several separate green carpels in the centre. The plant is a shrub with simple, alternate leaves.

There are three species of the scrubland shrub genus *Callicarpa* on this hillside: *C. loureiri, C. pedunculata* and *C. nudiflora*. They are similar in that all produce masses of small pink flowers in June that make a very showy inflorescence but differ in some small details such as leaf size, leaf margin and hairs. The leaf margins of the first two are finely toothed and the third minutely toothed. Rust-coloured hairs, particularly in young parts, appear in the first. Hairs are sparse on the second while they are a dense and velvety golden brown in the third. All three species have opposite, ovate leaves and attractive berry fruits. In *C. loureiri* they are white; in *C. pedunculata*, reddish-purple and in *C. nudiflora*, dark purple to black.

Callicarpa loureiri

85

A large, spiny sprawling shrub on the descending path is the False Custard (*Maclura cochinchinensis Lour. Corner*). The leaves are broadly ovate with toothed edges arranged spirally. Large spines occur in the leaf axils. The small, greenish-yellow flowers, either male or female, are formed in compact globular heads in the leaf axils. In the female the outer part becomes fleshy and the flowers fuse to form a compound, orange-yellow fruit not unlike the Custard Apple (*Annona reticulata*).

The orange-flowered *Cratoxylum ligustrinum* may still be in bloom, though *Itea chinensis* will not be. These trees are typical woodland species, indicating that scrubland is running out. Two woodland shrubs also common here are *Maesa perlarius*, showing sprays of green fruits, and the False Sumac (*Brucea javanica*). The False Sumac is about 1.5 metres high with alternate once-pinnate leaves and toothed leaflet margins. The leaflets feel soft and velvety due to a fine coat of yellow hairs. In June, it produces long axillary, spike-like inflorescences that are usually made up of small unisexual purplish flowers. It has an egg-shaped fruit that is at first green and later black. The ripe fruit is bitter-tasting and poisonous, but has various medicinal uses. It is said to cure amoebic dysentery, malaria and haemorrhoids and even gets rid of warts and corns. It grows all along the path leading to the village of Lung Mei Tau.

On reaching the village, you will find a cafe where you can buy drinks. Take a right turn in the village, opposite the cafe, and walk along a path in front of some houses. You pass through a glade lined by an aromatic shrub, the Negundo Chaste-tree (*Vitex negundo*). Despite being called a tree, the shrub is no more than about one to two metres high, although it may reach about four metres in ideal situations. The whole plant, apart from the upper surface of the leaves, is covered by short grey hairs, which make it velvety to the touch. The palmately compound leaves are in opposite pairs with three leaflets but leaves with five leaflets also occur. The Negundo Chaste-tree flowers in June. There appear to be two varieties: one has white flowers splashed with purplish-blue, which is the most common, and the other has purplish-blue flowers. The flowers are small. The five petals are joined to form a bell-shaped corolla with five lobes, one being longer than the others. All parts of this plant are used in Chinese medicines for curing various infections.

The path now runs along the side of a tidal stream that is lined by mangrove plants such as *Excoecaria agallocha* and *Clerodendrum inerme*. Eventually, it leaves the stream and passes through a small area of woodland. There is a large tree of a species of *Erythrina* that casts a pleasant shade. It has very large palmately compound leaves with long stalks. Growing nearby are some trees of the Chinese Hackberry (*Celtis sinensis*), a medium-sized tree with a spreading crown. The oval leaves are alternate, with the margin toothed towards the tip. At this time of year, there are one or two small, green fruits which ripen to dull orange-red.

This hardy tree is common throughout Hong Kong as a woodland species.

Eventually the path you are on comes out at a restaurant on the beach. The stream that your path follows flows in front of this restaurant before reaching the sea. To the right of the restaurant and in front of it, can be found some typical sandy-beach plants.

There is a large area of *Vitex rotundifolia*. In front of it is a very spiny grass called Littoral Spinegrass *(Spinifex littoreus)* usually growing in the area between low and high tide, although here it is well above the high tide mark. It certainly is well-adapted to growing in sand, into which it spreads by means of underground rhizomes (rootlike stems.) It has sharply pointed leaf blades which protect this grass from being eaten by grazing animals.

Littoral Spinegrass
Spinifex littoreus

Growing in the sand here and there on the beach, is a monocotyledon with white flowers. St John's Lily *(Crinum asiaticum)* is a bulbous herb with strap-like leaves arising from the bulb. The thick flowering axis terminates in an umbel of many attractive lily-like flowers, with parts in whorls of three. This plant belongs to the Daffodil Family, Amaryllidaceae. The fruit is a capsule that splits open to free large seeds which do not survive for long. However, under suitable wet and aerated conditions, they develop rapidly into new plants.

Two species typical of beach flora are scattered about among the *Spinifex littoreus* grass and the *Vitex rotundifolia*. These are a member of the Daisy Family (Compositae) called the Cocklebur *(Xanthium strumarium)* and a member of the Sugar-beet Family (Chenopodiaceae) called the American Wormseed *(Chenopodium ambrosioides)*.

The Cocklebur is a herb with spiral, broadly triangular, often three-lobed leaves which are wider than they are long. The stems are very hairy and the leaf margins are irregularly toothed. In June, the plant is usually covered with hairy achenes which are preceded by scaly flowerheads that are either male or female. Usually in the Compositae there are many tiny flowers grouped together in the head, but the Cocklebur is rather unusual in that the number is much reduced. In female heads there are only two tiny white flowers.

The American Wormseed is an aromatic annual that grows to a height of about one metre. If any part is crushed it gives off a strong aromatic smell. The plant is covered with white glandular hairs and as a result looks grey-green. The main stem gives rise to many side branches covered densely with small lance-shaped leaves with a toothed margin. It is not a particularly attractive plant even when it is flowering in June. The flowers are small and green, in leafy spikes. However, it is a noticeable member of the beach flora.

Behind the plants growing in sand along the seashore is a very attractive species of Clerodendrum in bloom. This is the Fragrant Glory-bower *(Clerodendrum fragrans)*. It covers fairly large areas and appears quite happy to be growing in very sandy soil, although it is not a typical beach plant. It has opposite heart-shaped leaves with almost entire margins, hairy underneath and rough to the touch. The flowers are formed in terminal compact clusters and are most unusual in that there are many whorls of petals. The flowers look rather like those of the rambler rose and are a delicate shade of pink fading to white with age. They have a delightful perfume. There is also a

Fragrant Glorybower
Clerodendrum fragrans

single-flowered variety, presumably the original wild form, but the double variety seems to be just as common especially around villages. It may well be a garden escape. The Fragrant Glorybower is used in Chinese medicine for the treatment of skin diseases.

A rather curious plant growing at the back of the beach is *Caesalpinnia crista* (see photograph on p. 77). Like some other members of this genus, it is a scrambling shrub, using the claw-like spines it has all over its stems, leaf-stalks and leaf midribs to hook onto other plants for support. The leaves are large and bipinnately compound, with about six pairs of leaflets, each divided again into five pairs of pinnules. It does not flower in June, but some plants which appear to have died have produced many flat pods covered with short spines. Some of these pods have split open down one side to reveal two grey seeds looking like two bird's eggs in a nest.

Well behind the beach is an area of shrubs. These include some Screw Pine, *Brucea javanica*, *Lantana camara* and *Clerodendrum inerme*, seen in Chek Keng. There are even a few plants of the Castor Oil Plant (*Ricinus communis*). It is an area where mangrove plants and seashore plants are jumbled together with plants often found on waste ground near villages. If you go far enough back from the seashore, where there is a low-lying area, the mangrove plants become more dominant. Here, the land is covered by the sea at high tide. A few trees occur in the mixed zone, such as *Rhus chinensis* and *Celtis sinensis*, but nothing much else.

Retrace your footsteps to Chek Keng where you will catch the ferry. On the way back you may see a small aquatic plant flowering in a stream that crosses the path. It is a species of *Torenia*, of which there are five listed for Hong Kong. The plant grows in the water and the blue flowers are quite small. Nearby are two species of *Selaginella*, *S. delicatula* (Desv.) Alston and *S. heterostachys* Baker. These club mosses have small leaves of two sizes, arranged in opposite pairs on the stem, a small leaf being opposite a large one. The latter species has very small leaves compared to the former and they are spaced out along the stem. Among the *Selaginellas* is *Pronephrium simplex*, a fern with a simple, undivided frond, rather unusual among ferns which often have much divided and even filigree leaves.

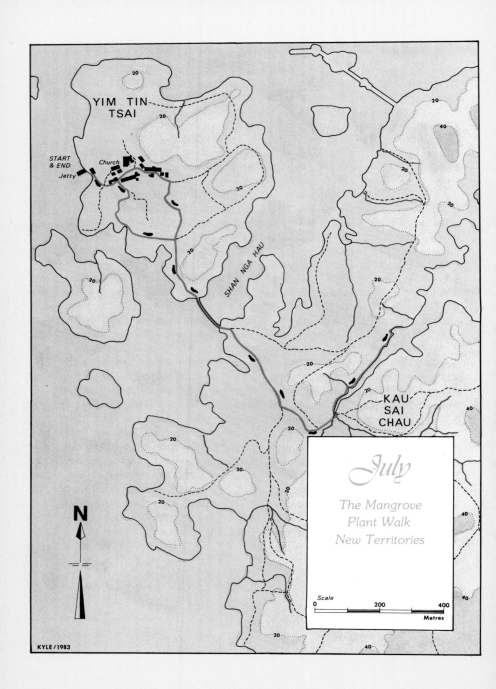

YIM TIN TSAI

START & END
Jetty
Church

SHAN NGA HAU

KAU SAI CHAU

N

July

*The Mangrove
Plant Walk
New Territories*

Scale

0   200   400

Metres

KYLE / 1983

July

The route in brief

Mangrove plants grow in the intertidal zone and are inundated by the sea twice a day. To see mangrove flora in their natural habitat, travel by bus or car to Sai Kung in the New Territories. Parking space is usually available except on Sundays near the new jetty or on the fringe of the old part of the village. There are plenty of sampans and some small junks for hire at the new jetty. Sharing the boat with other passengers will cost less. Make arrangements for the return trip, but do not pay boatmen until the return journey.

The 15-minute boat ride takes you past Sharp Island (on your right) and several other small islands. The scenery is delightful: a foreground of busy fishing boats against a background of mountains on the mainland including Ma On Shan. As you approach the jetty on the island of Yim Tin Tsai, you will see a white church tucked behind some trees. This is the only church in this area and is believed to be about a hundred years old.

On landing at the jetty, take the path to your right towards the village. Soon after the church (which is on your left) there is a path on your right. Follow it down to a flat, tidal area. Fork right and then left. At a T-junction turn right; the path leads to an embankment above the sea. Turn left on to it and follow through to a crossing of four ways, where you turn right. This path leads to a causeway between Yim Tin Tsai and Kau Sai Chau. After crossing it carry on to a long grassy area fringed by shrubs. Walk the length of this area and at the far end take the second path on your left. It leads down to the head of a mangrove valley. Follow the banks of this valley towards its mouth. Return by the same route.

91

The Walk

The focus of the walk is two small islands. The first has an ancient hamlet and a picturesque church set among the fish farms. The second — a much larger island — is reached by a causeway. You will walk across this causeway and then enter the mangrove swamp. There are plenty of shrubs growing here, even in the water itself, and in July you will see all the hill shrubs in flower. You can buy drinks in the village on the first island, but you should take food with you if you want to eat. This is a hot month so take a hat or umbrella against the sun.

On landing in front of a ramshackle, one-storey building, take a cement path that leads you under a large, umbrella-shaped tree, *Macaranga tanarius*. An evergreen tree that grows to about 5 metres in height, it is often planted in villages and on beaches to provide shade. It has large, broadly ovate, peltate leaves spirally arranged. These large leaves have given the tree its common name of Elephant's Ear.

Along the path are one or two plants of *Alocasia odora*, a herb with a tuberous underground stem from which arise large, waxy, heart-shaped leaves similar to those of rhubarb. The plants should be flowering, although what looks like a flower is really an inflorescence. One or two flowering stems occur in the axil of a leaf. On the upper part of these are groups of small flowers, female ones lowermost and male uppermost. These flowers are enclosed within a large green hooded structure called a spathe. The lower portion of the spathe forms an effective trap for insects such as flies until the inflorescence ages. When the trapped insects leave the inflorescence, they carry with them pollen which has rubbed off from the male flowers on their way out. The earlier ripening of the female flowers, and the position of the male flowers higher up on the inflorescence axis, favours cross-pollination. The inflorescence axis (spadix) is thick and fleshy, protruding beyond the region of the enclosed flowers as a pale green, rod-like structure marked with reticulate furrows. The enlarged spathe forms a hood over the whole inflorescence which looks like a single flower. Collections of red berries containing seeds follow the flowers.

Alocasia cucullata, another species of *Alocasia*, occurs in the village. A perennial herb, its leaves arise from an underground rhizome and resemble those of *A. odora* but are smaller.

Alocasia odora

The inflorescence has a short flowering axis and the fleshy spathe is about the same size as that of *A. odora*.

The path from the jetty curves to the left up a slight hill. You will find more Elephant's Ear trees and a large Yellow Camphor Tree *(Cinnamomum parthenoxylum)* about 10 metres high with vertically fissured grey-brown bark. The spiral oval-shaped leaves have entire margins and exude an aromatic camphor-like smell when crushed. This tree, which flowers in April, is closely related to the Camphor Tree *(Cinnamomum camphora)*, but may be distinguished from it by the larger, more robust leaves and the deeply furrowed bark.

The Yellow Camphor Tree is covered with a dense growth of Creeping fig, *Ficus pumila*, whose branches creep over the barks of trees, clinging on with numerous roots formed from the stem. The leaves are alternate in two rows, elliptic-shaped and leathery-textured. The margin is entire and recurved. Once this climber has a good hold on a support, it puts out horizontal branches that curve upwards. The leaves on these are much larger than on the creeping branches, though of a similar shape. In winter, the branches bear large figs, blackish-purple in colour with white dots when ripe. They are not good to eat as the contents are rather dry and full of tiny pips.

Just after the restaurant in the village is a cement path leading to the church. Services are still held here and the sense of serenity achieved by white walls and plain wooden pews is enhanced by the natural setting.

Near the main entrance is a Tallow-tree *(Sapium sebiferum)* whose branches are covered by Creeping Fig. The spiral leaves, shaped like spades in a pack of playing cards, are easy to recognise. This tree bears clusters of green fruits.

From the church walk back down the path you came up on and turn left. There are houses on your left and a row of Longan *(Euphoria longan)* trees on your right. A native of Southern China, this tree is grown by villagers for its edible fruit noted for its sweet fleshy pulp. It is similar to the Lychee tree but has much larger, untidy-looking leaves and a rougher, more corky bark. The leaves are spiral and once-pinnate, having up to five pairs of elongate leaflets. The leaflets are dark green above, but distinctly whitish below. In July the Longan fruit (in Chinese it means Dragon's Eye) should be forming in clusters. The rounded fruits have a yellowish-brown skin covering a white fleshy interior.

Longan *or* Dragon's Eye
Euphoria longan

Round about the path in the village is an attractive shrub, *Alchornea trewioides*, known as the Christmas Bush because the leaf stalk and the three main veins of the leaf are bright red. The leaves are spiral, again shaped like the spades in a pack of cards, and have a slightly serrated margin towards the leaf tip. It is a member of the Family Euphorbiaceae, to which the Poinsettia belongs. Many members of this family have unusually coloured leaves. The flowers of the Christmas Bush are formed in terminal spikes.

A common weed seen in areas of cultivation is the Smartweed *(Polygonum chinense)*, which has thick, fleshy, ridged stems. The leaves are alternate in two rows, of broadly ovate shape. It is not in flower in July, but produces dense heads of small white or pink flowers later in the year. Growing, presumably as a garden escape, is the Red Cluster Pepper (*Capsicum frutescens*, variety *fasciculatum*). It has clusters of small, red, conical fruits which, when dried, are the chief ingredient of local hot sauces.

Where the row of Longan trees ends, still just below the church, is a path on your right. It goes down to a flat tidal area controlled by a sluice gate. If you take this path you will see on your left a large tree, about 8 metres tall, of the Pomelo *(Citrus grandis)*. At this time of year it bears large green globose fruits, not yet fully ripe.

At the bottom of the path below the Pomelo tree fork right to cross the flat tidal area. In places it is covered by the Mangrove grass *(Zoysia sinica)*. One or two clumps of *Acrostichum aureum*, a mangrove fern which is rather rare in Hong Kong, occur in the middle of the tidal zone and a whole mass of it on the far side away from the village. A robust fern, it has a thick, erect rhizome that bears large once-pinnate, upright, rather leathery leaves unlike most ferns. The leaflets are strap-shaped, with blunt ends. Some of the leaves will have fertile leaflets towards the upper end of the leaf. Their under-surface is densely covered by brown sporangia. This distribution of the spore-forming organs all over one side of the leaf is known as the 'acrostichoid' condition and is regarded as the most highly evolved arrangement in ferns. Mostly sporangia are grouped into clusters called *sori* and are protected by a cover called an *indusium*. There is no cover here in *A. aureum*. This type of plan has developed independently in several unrelated groups of ferns, so is presumably sound for the survival of the species.

After taking the right fork you come to another fork. Bear left and go past several clumps of the Marsh Fleabane *(Pluchea indica)*. This is a plant found along muddy shores or the upper reaches of mangroves. It is a small branching shrub with alternate, ovate leaves with a margin that has short, narrow teeth. Leaf surfaces are hairy and the leaves thick and fleshy. In July the plant will be covered by terminal clusters of purple flower-heads. The outer florets are female and the inner ones bisexual. The fruit is an achene with a small parachute of hairs.

When the path comes to a T-junc-

Marsh Fleabane
Pluchea indica

tion turn right. You now climb on to a bank that overlooks an area of mud flats between low and high tide. There are a number of *Kandelia candel* bushes here that will be half covered by the sea if the tide is in, but completely exposed and surrounded by mud flats if it is out.

Kandelia candel (see photograph on p. 100) is a shrub with simple, opposite rather leathery leaves. In July it produces star-shaped flowers in cymose clusters of three to five in the leaf axils. The ovary is inferior and one-celled, having a three-lobed stigma. The seeds inside the fruit germinate before they ever become set free and the embryo plant inside puts out a young root that emerges from the fruit as an elongate green structure. The fruit and young projecting root are called a dropper. The dropper eventually falls from the parent plant and if the tide is out it will pierce the muddy soil below with its pointed end. If the tide is in it floats

in an upright position until it is carried to shallow water where it may become anchored in the mud. The droppers soon form side roots and develop into new plants. By this means, the plant is able to become established in the inhospitable intertidal zone where seeds would get washed away before they could germinate and become attached. Dropper formation is an essential part of plant adaptation to the mangrove habitat. Have a look around on this bit of mangrove and you are sure to find some young plants of *K. candel* that have recently developed from droppers. The droppers, hanging from the bushes, will not be seen until later in the summer, however.

Having had a good look at this mini-mangrove continue along the bank towards a bit of woodland which soon gives way to scrubland. Many shrubs are in bloom, for example, *Breynia fruticosa* with its greenish flowers, *Helicteres angustifolia* with pale pink flowers and *Wickstroemia indica* with small yellow flowers. Wild Coffee *(Psychotria rubra)* will be producing tiny white flowers in groups, as well as *Baeckea frutescens*, the latter looking very much like a white variety of Heather. The Glorybower *(Clerodendrum fortunatum)* is quite common, forming its unusual flowers with pink petals and persistent purple sepals. Bushes of *Melastoma sanguineum* are everywhere, often completely covered with their large pink flowers. *Melastoma candidum* is also in full flower.

Two shrubs are fruiting — *Phyllanthus emblica*, with green, gooseberry-like fruits all along its branches, and Rose Myrtle (*Rhodomyrtus tomentosa*) with hemispherical green fruits crowned with the persistent sepals. These will soon ripen to dark purple and may be eaten.

At the crossroads take the right which follows the coast of the island, now on your right, until you come to some steps leading down to a causeway joining Yim Tin Tsai to Kau Sai Chau. There are some Chinese Red Pine on your right just before the steps, and a Girl Guides Hostel on your left.

After crossing the causeway the path on the other side climbs a little and passes through more scrubland eventually coming out into a large flat grassy area used as a picnic site. This is almost completely encircled by a wall of small shrubs and trees, including *Sapium sebiferum, Schefflera octophylla, Rhus hypoleuca* and Screw Pine (*Pandanus tectorius*). *M. sanguineum* is very common, so this natural wall is embellished everywhere with its pink flowers.

Walk the length of the grassy area and at the end of it go through a break in the middle of the natural wall, ignoring a path on your left. A few metres further on you will see the beginning of a second path also on your left. This path will bring you along the side of a stream valley to the head of a much larger valley which has become a mangrove swamp.

Growing in the marshy ground is a plant rarely seen in Hong Kong. This is *Philydrum lanuginosum* or Woolly Grass, so-called because of its covering of whitish hairs. It has a short corm-like stem bearing long

Woolly Grass
Philydrum lanuginosum

sword-shaped leaves in two ranks, rather like the Gladiolus. The thick succulent leaves covered with woolly hairs ensheath one another at the base. The plant blooms in June, producing tall spikes of yellow flowers. Each flower is subtended by a large, leafy bract, spirally arranged. There are four petals, but only one stamen and a superior, unilocular ovary. The fruit is a three-valved capsule containing many seeds.

In this area a stream flows down from the low hills on your right into the mangrove valley. In the wet, marshy land close to this stream, two water-loving grasses, the Globose Twinball Grass (*Isachne globosa*) and the Indian Duck-beak (*Ischaemum ciliare, Retz*), may be found. *I. ciliare* is a slender grass with creeping and erect stems covered with long white hairs. The long narrow leaves are soft and hairy and drawn out to a point at the tip.

Follow the main stream down into the mangrove valley. Old plimsoles or running shoes are advisable as there is no clear path and the route is muddy. At first you will have to cross the stream, so that you are on the right bank, but later it is best to cross to the left bank where there is a ledge along which you can walk with ease.

The upper part of the mangrove is largely inhabited by various sedges (Family Cyperaceae). These are similar to grasses but have three-ranked leaves and three-sided stems; grasses are two-ranked and their stems are cylindrical. In July a tall flowering sedge that is very conspicuous on the mangrove is *Schoenus falcatus R. Brown, Prodr.* The three-ranked leaves ensheath one another so that the stem is hidden at the base. The sheaths are dark purple in colour. In cross-section the leaf blade is U-shaped and has a saw-like edge. If you run your fingers down the edge from the tip to the base you can feel the teeth, but in the opposite direction it feels smooth. The infloresc-ence is branched, with a series of leafy bracts alternating in two rows. There may be from four to ten such bracts, each with a partial panicle of brown spikelets in its axil.

Two other sedges are common, though much smaller. These are a species of *Eleocharis*, commonly called Spike Rush, and a species of *Fimbristylis*. Spike Rush has a creeping much-branched rhizome giving rise to tufts of slender green stems. The leaves are very reduced or absent. The stems terminate in tiny brown ball-like spikes of flowers. *Fimbristylis* has tufts of flowering stems arising from a rhizome. The leaves are reduced to sheaths only, as in *Eleocharis*. At the tip of the stem is an umbel of spikelets. These two sedges cover quite a large area of mud flats on both sides of the stream.

Continuing along the right bank, you see a number of rather spindly bushes of *Clerodendrum inerme*, a shrub found almost entirely along beaches or the upper reaches of

Eleocharis conjesta

Fimbristylis cymosa

mangroves. It has simple lanceolate, opposite leaves with entire margins. It may still be flowering in July, although April and May are the best months for this. The flowers are formed in groups of three in the leaf axils. They are white with a long tubular corolla which has five free lobes. There are only four stamens with purple filaments that stick out beyond the corolla tube, to which they are joined.

Soon you come to an area of Milky Mangrove *(Excoecaria agallocha)*, a tree confined to the seashore and the upper part of mangroves. In this area the plant is only about two metres high. The leaves are simple, ovate and spirally arranged. When crushed they exude a milky juice. Flowers may be seen in January, April, May, September and December. The plants are either male or female. The unisexual flowers occur in catkin-like groups in the leaf axils that stick upwards. The fruit is a three-lobed capsule.

Deeper into the mangrove two more typical mangrove swamp species, *Lumnitzera racemosa* and *Bruguiera conjugata*, are mixed with the Milky Mangrove. *L. racemosa* (see photograph on p. 100) can reach a height of 10 metres in tropical countries, but in Hong Kong it is never much taller than two metres. It has simple, spiral leaves that stick upwards so that the same amount of sunlight reaches both surfaces. The tip of the leaf has a notch in it, so they are described as emarginate. *L. racemosa* should be in flower, forming axillary racemes of small white flowers. There are five petals, ten

stamens that are attached to them, and a one-chambered ovary with three ovules. The fruit is elongated and woody with a single seed.

The Many-petalled Mangrove *(Bruguiera conjugata)* (see photograph on p. 100) is a small tree about 2 metres high, with simple, elliptic rather leathery leaves arranged in opposite pairs. There are stipules between the leaves, a characteristic of the Rhizophoraceae family to which it belongs. Most members of this family grow on mangrove swamps. The terminal buds of *B. conjugata* are protected by large pink-coloured bracts that drop off as the buds open. In July flowers may still be present, produced singly in the leaf axils. This plant forms droppers in a similar way to *Kandelia candel*. The part of the dropper derived from the ovary is a crimson red, but the rest is reddish-green and has longitudinal furrows (those of *K. candel* are green and smooth).

Soon a tributary to the main stream comes in from the right. Go across. The vegetation is now mixed mangrove and beach flora. You see Screw Pine *(Pandanus tectorius)*, Cuban Bast *(Hibiscus tiliaceus)* and Sea Lettuce *(Scaevola sericea)*. The Sea Lettuce and Cuban Bast tend to follow the high tide line along the shore on either side of the valley, but Screw Pine forms thickets in places, for example just after you cross the tributary.

A few plants of Spiny Bears Breech *(Acanthus ilicifolius)* (see photograph on p. 100) may be seen on the right bank of the main stream. It is an erect shrub with opposite, stiff and prickly leaves. The flowers, formed in terminal spikes, of a delicate purple shade with streaks of yellow in the lower lip, are generally seen from January to June and not often in July.

Some *Kandelia candel* bushes grow close to the Spiny Bears Breech and on the other side of the stream. Cross to the left bank and follow the stream down to the sea. The valley widens out and soon most of the plants you have seen are replaced by the Black Mangrove (*Avicennia marina*). This is a low-growing spreading shrub with opposite, ovate leaves of a rather bluish sheen and leathery texture; the under-surface is white due to bladder-like hairs. When the tide is high these bushes will be totally covered. Ideally, choose a day when low tide is at about noon.

A. marina is well adapted to withstand the effect of salty water. The strength of its cell sap is so high that it can still absorb water from the sea. Most plants can't, and lose water under such conditions. Its leaves are equipped with salt-secreting glands to get rid of the excess salt. Mangroves grow in very poorly aerated soil and have developed special breathing roots called pneumatophores that stick up into the air from the underground cable roots. These vertical breathing roots may be seen in radiating lines surrounding the central bushes of *A. marina*. They absorb oxygen from the air and get rid of carbon dioxide.

Growing among *A. marina* is another mangrove plant — *Aegiceras corniculatum* — with simple opposite leaves of a leathery texture. By July its fruits have ripened and are now becoming droppers. The droppers are curved and are much smaller than those of *B. conjugata*. They are scattered over a large area of the mangrove, often growing amidst other species.

To return, retrace your steps back up the mangrove valley. It is pleasant to walk in the stream as the bottom is firm. At the innermost end of the valley take the same path back to the causeway joining Yim Tin Tsai to Kau Sai Chau. On Yim Tin Tsai you may like to vary your walk to the village. When you get to the crossroads of paths walk straight over (a left turn would bring you back the way you came). This takes you round the other side of the flat tidal area where you saw the Mangrove Fern (*Acrostichum aureum*) at the start of the walk. Here on the left side of the path you will find a patch of Water Hyacinth (*Eichhornia crassipes*). It can grow as a floating plant, but in this area is found on the surface of mud. There is a rosette of heart-shaped leaves with long stalks. In aquatic specimens the stalk is greatly inflated, made up of an aerated tissue, serving as a flotation device, but these bladder-like petioles are not formed when it grows on land. It should be flowering in July, showing attractive spikes of violet-purple flowers. This plant is regarded as a pest in many countries, where it may cause the blockage of waterways, but in Hong Kong it is often used as fodder.

Walk back to the village with the church, and you will be ready to board your boat which will ferry you back to Sai Kung.

Lumnitzera racemosa

Spiny Bears Breech
Acanthus ilicifolius

Many-petalled Mangrove
Bruguiera conjugata

Kandelia candel

Meyen's Clematis
Clematis meyeniana

Sulphur Orchid
Habenaria linguella

Buttercup Orchid
Spathoglottis pubescens

Phantom Orchid
Habenaria dentata

101

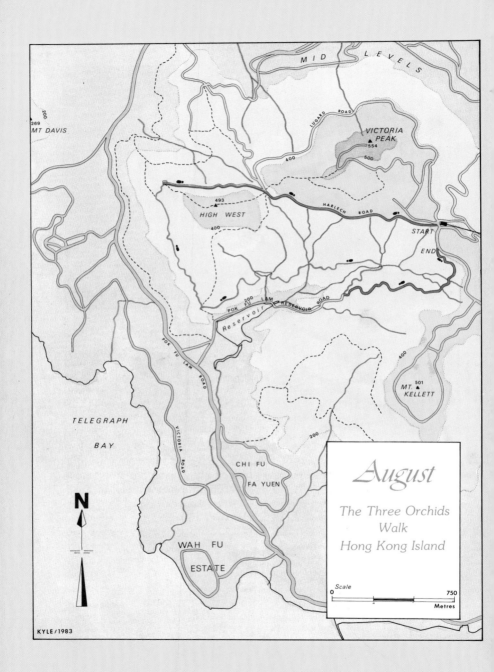

MID LEVELS

LUGARD ROAD

VICTORIA PEAK
▲ 554

500

400

MT DAVIS
▲ 269
200

493 ▲
HIGH WEST
400

HARLECH ROAD

START

END

POK FU LAM RESERVOIR ROAD
200

Reservoir

MT. ▲ 501
KELLETT
400

POK FU LAM ROAD

200

TELEGRAPH

BAY

VICTORIA ROAD

CHI FU

FA YUEN

N

WAH FU

ESTATE

KYLE/1983

August

*The Three Orchids
Walk
Hong Kong Island*

Scale
0   750
Metres

102

August

The route in brief

The circular walk around High West, one of the highest peaks on Hong Kong Island, gives you fine views of Hong Kong Harbour and the surrounding seascapes to the south and west. On the walk you will be charmed by the blooms of three of Hong Kong's wild orchids — two yellow and one white. The flowers of many hill shrubs and climbers can also be enjoyed. Take plenty of water to drink; walking at this time of year can be thirsty work. Some of the paths are rough so wear good walking shoes, and take a hat as much of the walk is in the open.

Take the tram from Central to the Peak. From the station, walk over to Harlech Road and follow it around Victoria Peak until you reach a grassy area below High West Mountain. Take two left forks to bring you on to a cement path which leads around the north side of High West to a look-out point. Here, on the far side of a terrace, are steps leading down to a hill path. Follow it around High West above Pok Fu Lam Road. It passes Queen Mary Hospital keeping more or less at the same level. After passing the Sulphur Orchid growing in a grassy area on your right, the path curves left around the mountain. You are now above Pok Fu Lam Reservoir, which is on your right. The path crosses about nine streams before traversing the main stream of a valley from the Peak down to the reservoir, after which it doubles back on itself down steps keeping parallel with the main stream. Eventually the path leaves the stream and joins the Reservoir Road. Turn left on to it and follow it up to where it joins Peak Road, close to where you started. Return to Central via the Peak Tram.

103

The Walk

From the Peak station, walk over to Harlech Road, which commences alongside the Peak Garden restaurant, and follow it. On your right is a cliff face, while on your left woodland drops below, following the steep slope of the land. There are a number of common local trees including the two species of Sumac, *Rhus chinensis* and *Rhus succedanea*, sometimes called the Wax Tree. *Acronychia pedunculata*, a member of the citrus family, bears sprays of small green fruits in the leaf axils, usually four per spray. The lacy-leaved White Popinac tree *(Leucaena leucocephala)* is common at the beginning of Harlech Road, and the Chinese Hackberry *(Celtis sinensis)* with its simple, ovate leaves, may also be seen quite frequently.

Two of the local trees producing large pods as fruits are the Yellow Poinciana *(Peltophorum pterocarpum)* and the Lebbeck Tree *(Albizia*

Yellow Poinciana
Peltophorum pterocarpum

lebbek). The Yellow Poinciana is a medium-sized deciduous tree with graceful, feathery bipinnate leaves. Large, flat, dark red pods will be seen on the tree in August. The strongly perfumed flowers, which form in the spring, are bright yellow with crumpled and twisted petals. The Lebbeck Tree is much larger with a wide-

Wax Tree
Rhus succedanea

Lebbeck Tree
Albizia lebbek

spreading crown. It has bipinnate leaves and in August will be seen bearing large strap-shaped pods. It flowers in April or May, forming pom-pom-like collections of greenish-yellow flowers, the long stamens of which are a most conspicuous feature.

The views to your left along Harlech Road are very fine. Below you stretches an unbroken expanse of evergreen forest that continues down to the Pok Fu Lam Reservoir.

An interesting shrub along the road is the Wild Kumquat *(Fortunella hindsii)*, with oval-shaped, spirally arranged leaves that have sharp spines in their axils. When crushed the leaves smell of citrus fruits. In August oval-shaped green fruits are present. Later these ripen to an orange colour and may be eaten. Herbs along the road include Lily Turf *(Liriope spicata)* with grass-like leaves and spikes of mauve flowers, and *Desmodium heterophyllum*, with tripinnate leaves and racemes of purple pea-like flowers. *Ixeris sonchifolia* has a rosette of fresh green leaves and a branching inflorescence of yellow flowerheads.

After about ten minutes' walking the road turns sharply to the right. On your left is a flat area of cut grass with a public shelter where you can sit in the shade. The peak of High West is on the far side of this grassy patch. The road soon forks; take the left fork which is the continuation of Harlech Road. Almost immediately it forks again. On your right is Hatton Road, but you must again take the left fork. It is a good cement path leading round the north side of High West. At first it passes through a

Lily Turf
Liriope spicata

cutting, but soon becomes a ledge path with a rock face on your left and a sheer drop on your right. On this side you have excellent views of the west end of Hong Kong harbour.

The vegetation along this path consists mainly of bushes not higher than nine feet. An attractive, slender shrub in bloom is Mountain Sesame *(Helicteres angustifolia)*. It has simple, alternate, oval leaves with two or three delicate pink flowers in each leaf axil. The fruit is covered with rust-brown hairs and splits into five valves to shed the seeds.

Stunted trees typical of scrubland include Rough-leaved Holly *(Ilex asprella)*, Round-leaved Litsea *(Litsea rotundifolia)*, the common Sumac *(Rhus hypoleuca)* and the Hairy Mountain Fig *(Ficus hirta)*. Among the typical woodland tree species are two other kinds of fig, the Green-fruited Fig (*Ficus variegata*, variety *chlorocarpa*) and the Rough-leaved Stem Fig *(Ficus hispida)*. The former is very common in mixed woods in Hong Kong and may be easily recognised in August by the green figs on the trunk. They exude a milky juice when picked. The leaves are heart-shaped, alternately arranged, with a pointed tip. The upper surface is smooth and shiny, but the under-surface is usually dull and covered with dots. The figs are rounded and hairless. The Rough-leaved Stem Fig has hairy opposite leaves of oval shape with a toothed margin. The figs are usually borne in twos on short stalks in the leaf axils. They are yellow, hairy and spotted.

At the side of the path in one place is a small specimen of the Scarlet Sterculia Tree *(Sterculia lanceolata)*. In August this tree bears its remarkable fruits. Each flower gives rise to five follicles (pod-like structures that split down one side only) that are at first green, then yellow, later still orange and finally brilliant scarlet. When they split on the lower side of each follicle, two rows of jet-black seeds, about the size of peas, are revealed. Two halves of the follicle curve upwards so that the seeds are fully exposed. The flowers are formed in slender panicles arising from the leaf axils from December to May. They are small and pink-coloured. The leaves are unremarkable.

After walking about half a kilometre along the cement path, more or less following the contour of the mountain, you will come to a lookout point. It is a flat grassy terrace with seats where you can sit. You can look out over the sea towards the western end of the New Territories, with Lantau in the far distance to your left. Cross the terrace to the far side and

Mountain Sesame
Helicteres angustifolia

you will find some steps leading downwards to a narrow but good hill path that at first passes underneath electric wires supported by metal pylons.

Not far below the lookout terrace and near the foot of the steps, you will come across several specimens of the Phantom Orchid *(Habenaria dentata)* (see photograph on p. 101), the first of the three orchids to be seen on this walk. It is a ground orchid with three to five stalkless oblong leaves, bluntly pointed with a smooth margin, arranged spirally on the flowering axis. The flowering axis bears from eight to eighteen pure white flowers at the upper end, perhaps with a touch of green at the tips of the perianth. The largest perianth segment forms a three-lobed structure called the labellum (equivalent to a petal) that serves as a landing stage for insects, and on either side there is a perianth segment (equivalent to a sepal), spread out in the same plane. The midlobe of the labellum is narrow and smooth but the side lobes are fringed with quite large teeth. The flower bears a spur with a kink in it, at the base of which is a nectary. The only pollinating insects that can reach the nectar must have a tongue at least 4 cm long, which is good news for moths or butterflies.

The pollen is in two pollen bags called pollinia, seen as two yellow blobs in the flower centre forming part of a knob-like structure called the column, the most characteristic feature of an orchid. It is a composite reproductive structure containing pollen, style and stigma. In this orchid the column is found protected below a hood formed from two petals and one sepal.

The vegetation in this area is hill scrubland containing a number of tree species. Present is the rare *Pentaphylax euryoides*, now producing terminal panicles of green oval fruits. It is one of several unique species found only on Hong Kong Island and may be regarded as a relic of the lost forests that have survived only in protected areas. Here and there along the path one finds a few specimens of the Spiny Date-palm *(Phoenix hanceana)*. It has a straight trunk covered with old leaf bases and crowned with a tuft of large, once-pinnate leaves. Some of the leaflets are spine-like, making the whole plant very prickly. In August candelabras of fruits develop on female plants. The fruit is at first bright orange but later turns dark brown. It contains fleshy edible material, but far less than the cultivated date.

In non-wooded parts of the track one may see the Hong Kong Heather or Dwarf Mountain Pine *(Baeckea frutescens)*. Its tiny pointed leaves are arranged in pairs on the twig-like branches and these, together with the flowers, give it a strong resemblance to the European white heather. The leaves contain aromatic oil glands. Also seen frequently is the Twig-hanging Embelia *(Embelia laeta)*, its trailing branches hanging over the path but no longer bearing fruits. The Hong Kong Hawthorn *(Rhaphiolepis indica)* is also common here. Now it is bearing green fruits that turn black when ripe. The False Groundnut *(Desmodium heterocarpon)*, with alternate, tripinnate leaves and pink pea-like flowers is also present.

Among climbing plants perhaps the most noticeable is Meyen's Clematis *(Clematis meyeniana)* (see photograph on p. 101), which is producing great bunches of white flowers with four petal-like sepals that are pale mauve on the under-side. True petals are absent. The leaves are tri-pinnate arranged in opposite pairs. The Glittering-leaved Millettia *(Millettia nitida)* is another climber blooming all along the path. It has alternate, once-pinnate leaves with five leaflets, the terminal one being slightly larger than the others. The purplish-pink, pea-like flowers are formed in terminal racemes. The standard petal at the back of the flower has a central yellow-green spot, probably there to attract bees to pay a visit and bring about cross-pollination. However, pollination often seems to fail as many of the flowers fall without setting fruit; the fruit is a hairy pod.

The Sandpaper Vine *(Tetracera scandens (L) Merr.)*, very common on this hillside, is a woody creeper with leaves that feel very rough to the touch, hence the common name. It was used by village housewives to scour out saucepans. The leaves are alternately arranged, broadly oval in shape with toothed margins and a bluntly pointed tip. In August there are panicles of small, fragrant white flowers. The fruit is at first white, but later red and hairy with a short beak. The climbing branches of this plant twist around any support that is available, forming thick impenetrable masses. Another common woody climber is the Scandent Rosewood *(Dalbergia hancei)*, which climbs by

the tips of its branches forming claw-like hooks around supports. The leaves are alternately arranged, and are once-pinnate. It forms small, white pea-like flowers in March, so will not be seen in bloom in August. The fruit is a one-seeded pod.

Two blooming herbaceous plants along this path are the common Adenosma *(Adenosma glutinosum)* and the Angle-stemmed Hedyotis *(Hedyotis acutangula)*. The former has simple, opposite hairy leaves with a wrinkled surface and toothed margins. The purple Foxglove-like flowers occur singly in the leaf axils towards the tips of the branches. The fruit is a capsule. The Angle-stemmed Hedyotis, as the name suggests, has four-sided stems that are square in cross section. The small white flowers are formed in terminal cymes in large numbers.

The hill path you are following winds up and down as you go, but in the main keeps you at about the same elevation. You are approximately half-way up High West mountain from Pok Fu Lam Road. As the path takes you round the north-west side of High West you will have very good views first of Mount Davis and later of Queen Mary Hospital. Your path runs more or less parallel with Pok Fu Lam Road. Lantau Island is visible on the horizon.

At length you will find yourself above a flat area of grassland. This is a cover to one of the filter beds where water is treated before being piped to the flats below. Take a path to the right down to this flat, grassy area where you will find the Sulphur Orchid *(Habenaria linguella)* (see photograph on p. 101) growing to profusion in the grass. It will be at its best in the early part of August. This orchid, approximately 15 cm in height, has about five narrow, dark green leaves spirally arranged. The flowering axis bears a raceme of eight to thirty-five sulphur-yellow flowers towards its tip, each flower carrying a spur which is thickened and green towards the lower end where the nectary is. When the flowers die the perianth persists for a while and turns chocolate brown. The fruit is a capsule, splitting open to shed many tiny seeds.

Growing cheek by jowl with the Sulphur Orchid is the Sensitive Plant *(Mimosa pudica)*, a scrambling shrub with spiny stems. The leaves are alternately arranged and twice-pinnate. These leaves are quite remarkable; when touched the pinnules fall back, followed by the leaflets. Finally the leaf stalk falls back too, so that the whole leaf has collapsed. Such movements, the mechanism of which is not fully understood, are made to scare off browsing animals. The flowers are formed in ball-like groups at the end of stalks axillary to the leaves. They are made conspicuous by their long, projecting, pink stamens, usually ten per flower. The fruit is a segmented pod.

Return to the hill path. Continue in the same direction by taking a right turn on to it from the filter bed. Pok Fu Lam Reservoir is now below you on your right. Soon you will find the third orchid on this walk. The Buttercup Orchid *(Spathoglottis pubescens)* (see photograph on p. 101), seen in large numbers in the bank on your left, is probably the most common ground orchid in Hong Kong and is usually found among grass. Each plant has two to four long, thin pleated leaves arising from a corm-like tuber just beneath or at the surface of the ground. The flowering axis terminates in a raceme of up to twenty blooms. Each flower has three buttercup-yellow sepals and two similar petals. The third petal is three-lobed, being the labellum, although in this orchid it is smaller than the other two petals. The midlobe is shaped like a violin with a ridge running down the middle and an orange-coloured lump on either side. The tip is notched. The column is not hidden under a hood as it was in the other two species of orchid. Sprays of these orchid flowers delight the eye.

The hillside is now thickly covered by False Camellia *(Gordonia axillaris)* above and below the path. In winter these small, evergreen trees will be covered with large Camellia-like flowers, turning the hillside white. In August only the woody fruits are to be seen. Another common tree is the Round-leaved Litsea, easily recognised by the pairs of small, green fruits developing in the leaf axils. All of the trees already recorded on the north side of High West are also present on these southern slopes.

One tree occurring here is Reevesia *(Reevesia thysoidea)*, a small tree not more than 5 metres high, with alternately arranged leaves of elliptical shape crowded together at the branch ends. It flowers from April to May and at that time the whole tree is covered with hemispherical clusters of white flowers, their stam-

Reevesia thysoidea

inal tubes protruding like pins in a cushion. In winter the five-angled fruits scatter winged seeds.

Among the climbing plants are Wild Asparagus *(Asparagus cochinchinensis)* and Morinda *(Morinda umbellata)*. The Wild Asparagus climbs up other plants by twisting its stems around their branches. The stems bear flattened, green structures which serve as leaves although they are actually branchlets. In August it produces green fruits which are later greyish white or pink. Morinda often climbs to the top of small trees, which are seen to be covered by its orange fruits, irregularly shaped as they have been formed by the fusion of the ovaries of six or seven flowers. The leaves are oblong, arranged in pairs. The flowers of Morinda are small, inconspicuous, and formed in May.

At the beginning the path from the filter bed is open, but further along it is crossed by at least nine streams where trees and ferns occur. The Lamb of Tartary *(Cibotium barometz)*, to be found at the first stream, is a large fern with bipinnately compound leaves, but the specimens found here are small. The Scaly Fern *(Microlepia hancei)* is similar to the Lamb of Tartary in that the leaves are bipinnate but it is a much smaller fern and is not so hairy. The Fan-leaved Maidenhair Fern *(Adiantum flabellulatum)* likes moist shady places. The leaves have wiry, dark-coloured stalks with a lamina divided into three to four alternating leaflets that are divided again into several fan-shaped pinnules.

Several other ferns grow on the bank on the left-hand side of the path. In less shady places one finds *Notholaena hirsuta Desy*. The small triangular-shaped fronds are bipinnate (sometimes even tripinnate). The fertile fronds are slightly larger than the sterile ones with the *sori* (collections of spore-forming structures) spread out on the vein endings. This fern is closely related to the Narrow-leaved Lip Fern *(Cheilanthes tenuifolia)*, but is much more hairy. Another small fern on the bank is *Pteris multifida, Poir.* The frond is once-pinnate with a lamina made up of one to four pairs of lateral leaflets plus one terminal lance-shaped leaflet. The fertile fronds are slightly larger than the sterile ones, having sori spread out along the reflexed margins. This fern is common all along the path.

Follow the path round and slowly up the southern side of High West. In places there is a thick cover of bamboo, but towards the end it is all woodland. You can look up to the

110

Peak Restaurant and see the sweep of forest running down the mountain towards Pok Fu Lam Reservoir. One main stream drains this area, forming a fairly steep valley near to the reservoir. The path you are on crosses this main stream; it is about the tenth stream you cross. The others are only tributaries to the main stream, or lead directly into the reservoir.

Having crossed the main stream on stepping stones, turn right. The path now descends some steps, with the main stream on your right, but soon levels out. You are passing through woodland in heavy shade. Among the less common trees is *Garcinia oblongifolia*, which grows up to 15 metres in height. It has opposite ovate leaves with smooth margins and a blunt point. The flowers are greenish-white, formed in clusters in the leaf axils earlier in the year. The flower parts are in fours and the fruit a fleshy berry.

The conspicuous fruits of *Symplocos crassifolia* are to be seen. This tree has alternate, broadly ovate leaves that are tough and leathery with smooth margins. There are pairs (sometimes more than two) of oval green fruits in the leaf axils. The fruits ripen black and are fleshy but very bitter to the taste. There is a hard central portion like a stone in the plum or cherry. *Turpinia arguta* is a small tree, very noticeable because of the terminal panicles of hard green fruits containing about seven brown seeds. The leathery leaves are in opposite pairs, elliptical in shape with a toothed margin.

Pronephrium simplex, one of the ferns on the bank on your left, has a single tongue-like frond and can easily be recognised because it contrasts strongly with the twice-divided delicate fronds of *Adiantum flabellulatum*, with their fan-shaped pinnules. Mixed with the ferns in the heavy shade is *Selaginella trachyphylla* (named *S. atroviridis* in the *Hong Kong Check List*). This fern ally has two rows of small leaves on the upper side of the horizontal branches as well as two rows of larger leaves on either side. It is a club moss.

The path hugs the hillside on your left, and a ten-minute stroll from the main stream brings you to the reservoir road. Turn left on to it and continue uphill towards the Peak. At first there is a rock wall on your right with forest on your left. The road is partly shaded by trees. When you get to the last section of road, large trees occur again. Growing on your right above a wall are two large Chinese Banyans *(Ficus microcarpa)*. The roots of these trees form a network over and between the bricks of the wall. Look for hanging roots on the branches: they are very characteristic of this species. Finally the forest road joins the end of Peak Road, close to the Peak Tram Station.

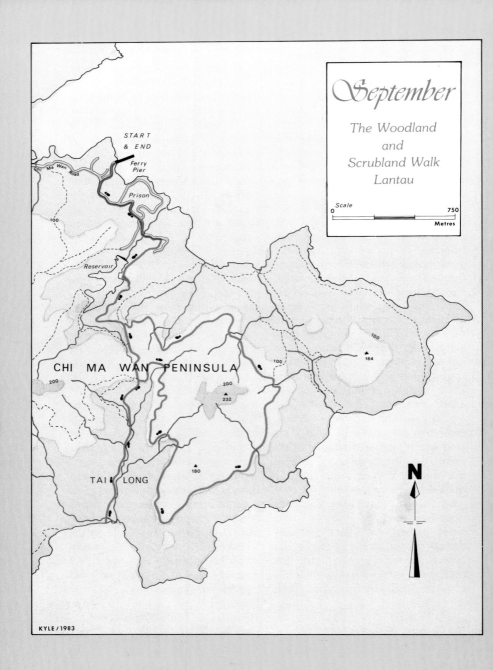

September

The Woodland
and
Scrubland Walk
Lantau

Scale

0   750

Metres

START
& END

Ferry
Pier

Chi Ma Wan Road

Prison

100

Reservoir

CHI MA WAN PENINSULA

200

100

100

164

200

232

TAI LONG

180

N

KYLE / 1983

September

The Woodland and Scrubland Walk
Chi Ma Wan Peninsula, Lantau
Time: 4 — 5 hours

The route in brief

T he peninsula of Chi Ma Wan on Lantau Island is an excellent example of what afforestation can do. Here you can wander through planted woodland of Brisbane Box, pines and Eucalyptus and enjoy the resinous aroma that fills the air. The trees are mirrored in the water of a reservoir where swallows catch insects on the wing. Leaving the woods the path takes you through rocky scrubland above the shoreline. Here Cheung Chau can be seen from unusual angles and the flowers and brightly coloured fruits of shrubs and climbers abound. A diversion to the village of Tai Long Wan allows you to discover delicate, shy herbs growing in disused rice terraces and to see the Ginger Lily in bloom.

Take the ferry from Hong Kong Island to Silvermine Bay on Lantau Island. From Silvermine Bay, catch a smaller ferry bound for Cheung Chau which calls at Chi Ma Wan. (Since ferries are infrequent, check ferry schedules before starting.) On landing at Chi Ma Wan take the road that goes inland above the closed refugee camp for Vietnamese. It curves to the left above the camp eventually reaching a prison gate. Take the steps on your right up round one corner of the prison. The path soon descends on the other side to a road. On your left is another prison gate. Turn right on to the road and follow it up between houses. It curves to the left over a bridge and ascends a hill between more houses. Take the dirt road on your right just before the crest of the hill. Follow it through woodland above the Prison Reservoir until it joins a path crossing it at an angle. Turn right on to this path. Almost at once on your left is another path that you will return on, but at present ignore this. Carry on along the main path until you come to a T-junction where you turn left. Within a few paces there is a fork. The right one takes you downhill on a diversion to Tai Long Wan while the left one follows a contour path around the hillside. After making the diversion return up the hill to the same point and turn right on to the contour path. Follow it as it winds in and out of the hillside until you are above the coast, where it bends to the left. At length you come to a fork; take the left one. This path leads you to the dirt road above the reservoir and you can return the way you came to the prison jetty.

The Walk

After you have passed the Vietnamese refugee camp and the corner of the prison, the road curves to the left across a bridge over an attractive stream bordered by Ginger Lily plants (Hedychium coronarium). These have two-ranked, lance-shaped leaves. In September it puts out spikes of pure white flowers whose strong, heady perfume can be smelt from afar. The flowers have only one fertile stamen; two infertile ones look like petals. There are six lobes to the perianth (petal-like parts) which forms a long tube below. This plant comes from India but is often grown in Hong Kong for its fragrant flowers.

The road takes you up a hill past some houses. Nearly at the top of the hill take the right. This rough road leads you above the prison reservoir. You will now pass through a woodland of introduced Acacia confusa, Brisbane Box (Tristania conferta) and Horsetail Tree (Casuarina equisetifolia), commonly planted because they are hardy and stand up well to exposed positions and hill fires.

Another introduced tree along the road is Swamp Mahogany (Eucalyptus robusta), which grows to about 10 metres and has dark brown, rough bark. The leaves, alternately arranged and oval-shaped, smell strongly of eucalyptus when crushed. In September, clusters of yellowish-white flowers in groups of three or more occur in the leaf axils. Among local trees in these woods are Turn-in-the-wind (Mallotus paniculatus), Mountain Tallow (Sapium discolor), Chinese Red Pine (Pinus massoniana) and Prickly Ash (Zanthoxylum avicennae).

Turn-in-the-wind is the most conspicuous because it flowers from August to September, producing large branched spikes of small strongly scented greenish-yellow flowers that lack petals. The leaves are spirally arranged with long stalks and a three-lobed leaf blade like that of the Maple. The dark green surface contrasts strongly with the white under-surface when ruffled by the wind. Rust-coloured hairs cover the stem and young parts. Mountain Tallow grows to about 5 metres high and in September bears green fruits which turn black when ripe and split open to set the seeds free. Chinese Red Pine, a source of both resin and turpentine in China, is common all along this path and fills the air with a resinous aroma. The Prickly Ash has characteristic toothed bark, prickly stems and once-pinnate leaves. The only other tree of note is the Smooth-barked Mempat (Cratoxylum ligustrinum). Its opposite, simple leaves are larger than usual in these woods.

Follow the earth road but watch

out for deep fissures due to soil erosion. You may see a bracket fungus on the trunk of a *Casuarina* tree. It is a species of *Polyporus*. The undersurface is pitted with pores from which fall spores in their millions. Such fungi are related to mushrooms and toadstools, where the spores are formed all over the surface of gills beneath the cap.

The earth road at length leaves the reservoir and joins a path that crosses it at an angle. Turn to the right on to this path. Almost at once, on your left, is a path that runs through some *Acacia confusa* trees. This is the path that you will return on, but for the moment ignore it. Carry on along the main path through woodland. Among the trees are two species of Sumac — *Rhus hypoleuca* and *Rhus chinensis* — both bearing similar flowers, small and cream-coloured in branched inflorescences, and distinguishable by their once-pinnate leaves. In *R. hypoleuca* they are white below and there is no winging on the midrib, while in *R. chinensis* they are yellow underneath and the leaf midrib is clearly winged.

In places where the woodland is fairly open shrubs such as Rose Myrtle *(Rhodomyrtus tomentosa)* and *Melastoma sanguineum* flourish. At this time of year they are fruiting. *M. sanguineum* has hairy fruits; the apex is flat and if broken open reveals orange-coloured seeds. Rose Myrtle fruits are berry-like, green when young but black when ripe, edible and taste somewhat like raspberries. The Myrobalan *(Phyllanthus emblica)* may also bear green to reddish globose fruits at this time. Although edible, they have a very acid taste like that of unripe gooseberries.

Several herbs flowering along the path include the Angle-stemmed Hedyotis *(Hedyotis acutangula)* with four-sided stems and small white flowers, *Elephantopus tomentosa*, with forking branches and tiny white flowers and the Purple Justicia *(Justicia procumbens)* with opposite, simple leaves and pinkish-purple, two-lipped flowers in a terminal spike. The flowers are formed in pairs in the axil of a leafy bract.

Look for the Creeping Psychotria *(Psychotria serpens)* now forming its opaque white berries, and the rare small-flowered Grewia *(Grewia biloba)*, a sprawling, low-growing shrub with alternate, simple, hairy leaves with toothed edges. In September it has umbels of small yellow flowers on stalks in the leaf axils. The Wild Raspberry *(Rubus reflexus)* with its prickly, spreading branches is now no longer fruiting but its dark red patterned, five-lobed leaves stand out.

Purple Justicia
Justicia procumbens

After about ten minutes' walking, the woodland path comes to a T-junction. Turn left on to a contour path which almost at once forks, one path continuing around the hillside, the other descending sharply to the village of Tai Long. You can either take a diversion here and walk down to the village or stay on the contour path. The walk down to the village follows a cement path, with some steps, through woodland. The commonest trees are Chinese Red Pine, Mountain Tallow, the Smooth-barked Mempat and the Chinese Sumac.

A striking shrub common along this cement path is *Phyllodium pulchellum*. It is no more than 1.5 metres high, with alternate, trifoliate leaves. The middle leaflet of the three is much larger than the other two. The under-surface of the leaflets is soft and hairy. In September the leaf axils bear flowering shoots, the flowers being hidden inside paired, rounded bracts, arranged alternately in two rows on the shoot. There are three or four small, yellow, pea-like flowers between each pair of bracts, and these are soon followed by one, two or three-jointed pods.

Various other shrubs are present in the undergrowth, such as the Rough-leaved Holly *(Ilex asprella)*, Wild Coffee *(Psychotria rubra)* with clusters of green berries that later ripen to red, Tea Gourd *(Pteroloma triquetrum)*, full of purple pea-like flowers, and the Fragrant Glory-bower *(Clerodendrum fragrans)*, very prominent with its clusters of pale pink, double flowers, looking like a rambler rose. Near the village is the

Negundo Chaste-tree
Vitex negundo

curious spiny shrub called the Thorny Wingnut *(Paliurus ramosissimus)*, as well as the Negundo Chaste-tree *(Vitex negundo)*, easily recognised by the palmately compound leaves with five leaflets and branching spikes of small, mauve-white flowers.

About half-way down to the village the woodland gives way to a flat area, formerly used for rice cultivation. The cement path runs along one side of this wet, muddy expanse, now almost exclusively colonised by the Globose Twinball Grass *(Isachne globosa)*. Its creeping stems branch profusely, bearing two rows of small, linear leaves. Where the leaf sheath joins the blade is a characteristic ring of white hairs. In September it produces panicles of nodular spikelets. The whole area is a sea of these waving, plume-like panicles.

Other grasses found here are Panic Grass *(Panicum brevifolium)*, which likes damp, shady spots and Redtop *(Rhynchelytrum repens)*, introduced from South Africa but now

116

established in Hong Kong. Panic Grass has unusually broad (for a grass) oval- to lance-shaped leaves arranged alternately in two rows. In September it forms panicles of oval shape on stems 50 cm tall . The spikelets are small, elliptical and pointed, often purplish coloured.

Redtop is one of the more attractive grasses, with hairy stems and elongate strap-shaped leaves in two rows. It can grow to about one metre high. In September it puts out flowering shoots capped by a loose panicle of pink, fuzzy spikelets. When the sun shines through them it can be seen that they are densely covered with pink hairs.

In the wet soil of the former rice-field grow a number of moisture-loving herbs. At least three of these belong to the Labiatae Family. In September they produce attractive mauve to purple flowers. A characteristic feature is the two-lipped corolla, the lower lip forming a landing stage for insect pollinators. Hyptis (Hyptis suaveolens) is a very hairy

Hyptis suaveolens

plant up to one metre high, with stout square stems and ovate leaves. The inflorescence axis bears paired, leafy bracts in the axil of which are many small mauve flowers clustered together and without stalks. Each flower has a bell-like calyx with fine spiny teeth enclosing the tubular, bilobed corolla. *Dysophylla auricularia*, also a very hairy herb, grows 50 cm high and has a square to rounded

Globose Twinball Grass
Isachne globosa

Dysophylla auricularia

117

stem. The paired leaves are ovate with a toothed edge. The inflorescence is a cylindrical spike of densely packed mauve flowers. A marked feature of the flower is the four prominent, feathery stamens covered with long hairs.

A mint called *Anisomeles indica* is also hairy, with square stems and paired ovate leaves with toothed margins and a pointed tip. The inflorescence is a terminal spike with clusters of almost stalkless mauve flowers in the axil of leafy bracts. The corolla is markedly bilobed, the lower lobe being much smaller than the upper. Another moisture-loving herb is *Lindernia cordifolia*, a member of the Foxglove Family and closely related to the Labiatae but having a different structure to the ovary of the flower. It is a low-growing, hairless plant, the branching stems being more or less prostrate. The paired leaves are ovate with a pointed tip; the stalk is very short or absent. The flowering stems are erect, with paired leafy bracts in the axils of which are single, stalked

Lindernia cordifolia

flowers forming a raceme. The corolla is white to pale mauve.

A contrast to the mauve-flowered herbs is the Primrose Willow *(Ludwigia octovalis)* (see photograph on p. 122), a large shrubby herb growing up to several metres high, and usually very hairy. The leaves are alternate and elongate with a pointed tip. The pale yellow flowers occur singly in the leaf axils and have four green sepals, four broad yellow petals and eight stamens. Another yellow-flowered herb growing close by is *Wedelia chinensis*, which has semi-prostrate stems rooting from the nodes. The paired leaves are lance-shaped with well-separated teeth on their margins. The small flowers are in solitary heads; both ray and disc florets occur. Orange butterflies of the genus *Potanthus* (probably *P. confucius*) visit these flower-heads to collect nectar. The White Smartweed *(Polygonum lapathifolium)* is common here. This is a hairless annual herb growing up to 60 cms high with

Anisomeles indica

erect branches bearing alternate broadly ovate leaves with a pointed tip. The small white flowers are densely grouped into cylindrical spikes borne at the tip of the stem and in the leaf axils.

The cement path drops down from the former rice paddy area quite steeply and soon you leave the wooded hillside and come out into the open. Close to a one-storey building with a tiled roof are large clumps of Triumfetta (Triumfetta bartramia), about one metre tall, on your left. This annual herb has alternate, hairy leaves of rhomboid shape, sometimes with three lobes and three main veins. The leaf edge is irregularly toothed and the under-surface greyish-green. The inflorescences, which occur in the leaf axils, are made up of nodular clusters of bright yellow flowers along the flowering shoot. The fruit, a globose capsule, is covered with hooked spines for dispersal by animals. Climbing up the Triumfetta with its spiralling stems is the Umbel-flowered Merremia (Merremia umbellata), a member of the Convolvulus Family (Convolvulaceae). The leaves are alternate and heart-shaped with entire margins and the flowers occur singly in the leaf axils, looking like white trumpets. The fruit is a small conical-shaped capsule.

Close by is India Abutilon (Abutilon indicum), a member of the Hibiscus Family, Malvaceae. It has delightful sulphur-yellow flowers borne singly in the leaf axils. The flower parts are in fives. The fruit is a curious ridged, hairy structure that splits into fifteen to twenty parts. The leaves of this herb are alternate and heart-shaped with irregular teeth in the margin.

Turn right at the building with the tiled roof and a few metres further on is Tai Long Wan village. Round about the village the Ginger Lily can be seen in bloom and bunches of it may be purchased. Below a local pub is a small field of Water Spinach (Ipomoea aquatica). A semi-aquatic plant, it grows best in swampy ground or even floating on the water surface. It can, however, grow on dry land. It has triangular-shaped leaves with long stalks. In September the white, trumpet-shaped flowers are present. Like the Umbel-flowered Merremia, it is a member of the Convolvulaceae. The boiled leaves simulate European spinach to which it is not botanically related.

From the village a cement path leads to a swimming beach enclosed by a fine sandy bay. It takes about thirty minutes to walk back up the hill from the village. The contour path winds in and out as it follows the line of the hills. It passes through woodland which consists mainly of Eucalyptus, a tall tree about 15 metres high, with spirally arranged, elongate lance-shaped leaves which hang downwards in a characteristic way. The woodland gives way to scrubland. Here you will see the Red Leaf of Autumn or Cow Vine (Rourea microphylla) with its young, red leaves opening out above the flowers (see photograph on p. 122). The mature green leaves are spirally arranged and once-pinnate, with nine pairs of leaflets plus a terminal one. Pale pink flowers form racemes in groups of five in the leaf axils.

Champion's Bauhinia (Bauhinia

championi) is a climbing shrub with alternate heart-shaped leaves that are split about one third to the base into two lobes. It forms large racemes of creamy white flowers borne terminally or in the leaf axils from September to October. The flowers give rise to oblong flat pods. Another climbing Bauhinia, *B. glauca*, also has two-lobed leaves and produces white flowers with pink stamens in May.

Clerodendrum viscosum is a shrub with paired broadly ovate leaves with plain margins. The inflorescence is a terminal panicle of cymose groups of flowers packed closely together. These groups are very showy in the September fruiting stage as the five sepals persist and become scarlet red in sharp contrast to the black berry-like fruit.

Noticeable on a ledge overlooking Tai Long Wan are the globose orange berries of a clump of *Strychnos angustiflora* (see photograph on p. 122), a shrub whose seeds, bark and young leaves contain strychnine. It has opposite, ovate leaves with three prominent veins. The curious Big-spine Honeylocust *(Gleditsia macrantha)* has alternate bipinnate leaves, usually with three pairs of leaflets, the terminal one being missing. In the leaf axils are large, red, branched spines; some are divided into three like a trident, others like a cross and still others may have five or more spiny branches, all effective protection against browsing animals. The plant belongs to the same family as Bauhinia.

Avoid a left turn from the main path, as this will lead you up a blind alley to a grave. Two climbing plants quite common along the contour path are *Gnetum montana*, an odd member of the Gymnosperms (pines and their allies), and the Sandpaper Vine *(Tetracera scandens)*. A less common climber here is Sour Creeper *(Ecdysanthera rosea)*. It has slender, twisting stems bearing simple, lance-shaped leaves in pairs. In September terminal panicles of small, five-petalled pink flowers occur. The fruit is made up of two elongate and pointed follicles placed at an obtuse angle to each other. They split open to set free oblong seeds crowned by a ring of short hairs for wind dispersal.

Once you are out of the woodland and there is more light you will find herbs along the path, including Common Bluebeard *(Caryopteris incana)*, which has paired, ovate, dull green and slightly hairy leaves with a pointed tip and toothed margin. The small flowers, of a delicate violet-blue shade, occur in dense cymose groups in the leaf axils. The fruit is a globose capsule.

Iron-weed *(Vernonia cinerea)*, an attractive member of the Daisy Family (Compositae), has alternate, oblong hairy leaves with a toothed margin. The tiny flowers are grouped into showy heads of bright purple arranged in loose groups. There is a species of *Ixeris* here with bright yellow flower-heads (only ray florets occur) and White Bush Aster *(Aster baccharoides)* with white ray florets and yellow disc florets in the centre of the flower-head. The Elecampane *(Inula cappa)* has just started to bloom. The Dog's Tail Bean *(Uraria macrostachya)* which blooms in June is now in fruit — a curious, twisted pod divided into two or three bulging sections each containing one seed.

The path turns to the left and follows the coast of the Chi Ma Wan Peninsula at a high level offering good views of Cheung Chau, first seen from one end but later seen in full length from the harbour side. The hillside, strewn with enormous boulders, is scrubland mixed with grassland.

A number of grass species are present, but two stand out — the Four-veined Eulalia (Eulalia quadrinervis) and the Green Foxtail (Setaria viridis) (see photograph on p. 122). The former is a stout grass with elongate tapering leaves (the margins are turned back when dry) and ribbed stems. The inflorescence is made up of two to four slender spike-like racemes. The stamens are pinkish, so this is the colour of the racemes. The Green Foxtail is a tufted grass about 60 cm tall with broadly elongate pointed leaves. The inflorescence is a spike-like panicle. The spikelets occur in the axils of bristle-like structures that make the whole thing look like a bottle brush.

After walking for some time, take a left fork which turns inland through planted woodland of Acacia confusa, Brisbane Box and Slash Pine (Pinus elliottii). This Pine can be distin- guished from the Chinese Red Pine because the needle leaves are longer and are grouped in threes instead of twos on the dwarf shoots. It is said to stand up better to forest fires than the local species. At one point the path crosses a small stream. Growing in the mud are Sundew (Drosera burmanni) and a species of Bladderwort (Utricularia) which has small strap-shaped leaves lying on the surface of the mud and tiny bladders to catch small insects like water fleas.

Towards the end of the path the woods consist entirely of Brisbane Box. A strange fungus sometimes found growing on the ground here is a species of Scleroderma, a Puff-ball Fungus (Gasteromycete) containing millions of spores. When cut across, the spore-forming portion in the centre is seen as a purplish-grey area while the flesh is yellow. Scleroderma fruit bodies (fructifications) are ovoid, smooth and light-brown in colour. They are attached to the soil by a short, thick 'root stock'. The path continues through an area of Acacia confusa trees until it rejoins the rough road that runs above the reservoir where you started the walk. It is now an easy matter to retrace your steps to the prison jetty to catch a ferry back to Silvermine Bay.

Green Foxtail
Setaria viridis

Primrose Willow
Ludwigia octovalis

Red Leaf of Autumn *or* Cow Vine
Rourea microphylla

Strychnos angustiflora

Monkeypod
Abarema clypearia

Ivy Tree
Schefflera octophylla

Grantham's Camellia
Camellia granthamiana

Acacia (left) and Eucalyptus (Swamp Mahogany) trunks
Acacia confusa and *Eucalyptus robusta*

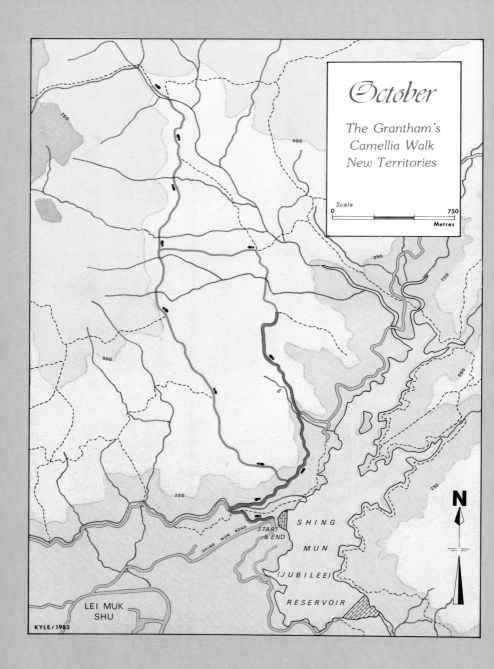

October

The Grantham's
Camellia Walk
New Territories

Scale

0 ——————————— 750

Metres

750

500

500

250

250

250

250

250

250

SHING

MUN

(JUBILEE)

RESERVOIR

SHING MUN ROAD

START
& END

LEI MUK
SHU

N

KYLE/1983

October

The Grantham's Camellia Walk
Tai Mo Shan and Jubilee
Reservoir, New Territories
Time: 5 — 6 hours

The route in brief

Grantham's Camellia, distinctive for having the largest flowers among the Camellia Family, grows on the south-eastern slopes of Tai Mo Shan in the New Territories. Discovered in 1955, it was named in honour of Sir Alexander Grantham, then Governor of Hong Kong. To see this rare bloom in its native habitat, you will have to make a trip to Tai Mo Shan in the New Territories and clamber up the banks of a stream.

Drive along the Shing Mun Reservoir Road via Tsuen Wan or take the Number 32 bus from the Tsuen Wan Ferry Pier. Just below the Jubilee dam, the first one you come to along the Shing Mun Reservoir Road, is a group of stalls selling food and drink. This is a convenient place to stock up for the day. Take the sealed path that is on the left as you come up to the dam. It turns backwards, almost in the direction of the road you have come up on and goes past the stalls, which are now on your left. There is an open bar-type restaurant on your right. Parking is available at the upper dam further along the Shing Mun Reservoir Road. The sealed path becomes the so-called jogging trail. Follow it for about 100 metres to an iron bridge over a water catchment on your right. Cross this bridge and carry on along this forestry road for about half a mile. There are a number of paths on your left along this road. Take the fifth one just after a hairpin bend. Where this side road becomes a natural path through woodland it crosses several streams, and further along you must fork left twice. The second left fork becomes a steep path ascending the slopes of Tai Mo Shan. At the end of this path is a T-junction. Turn right along a contour path that crosses several small streams. At length it joins the main stream in which *Camellia granthamiana* grows. Turn left up the stream, clambering over boulders in the stream bed. About 100 metres up the stream, on the right-hand side, is the single tree of *Camellia granthamiana*. Return by the same route along the contour path. When you get to the steep path down, now on your left, ignore it and carry on along the contour path. At length it descends by many steps to the forestry road you started on, so by turning right on to it you can retrace your steps back to the lower dam, and return by bus or car.

The Walk

Walk about 100 metres up the waterworks access road from the dam and you will come to an iron bridge that crosses the water catchment channel on your right. Almost opposite the bridge there is a country parks picnic area, pleasantly shaded by several trees. There is a good specimen of the Camphor Tree *(Cinnamomum camphora)*, a member of the Laurel Family. A native of Hong Kong, the tree is characterised by a dense crown of shining dark-green leaves and a trunk crisscrossed by vertical cracks and fissures. The oval-shaped leaves have one main vein and two large lateral veins. At the junction of the lateral veins and the main vein is a gland producing the volatile camphor oil which gives off a strong smell when the leaf is crushed. Oil can also be obtained from the wood and roots. In April, small yellowish flowers are formed, followed by small, black, fleshy, one-seeded fruits. Other trees that can be seen at this site are the Horsetail Tree *(Casuarina equisetifolia)*, and the Chinese Red Pine *(Pinus massoniana)*.

Cross the iron bridge over the water catchment channel. On the left-hand side is a good specimen of the Golden Dewdrop *(Duranta repens)*. It is an introduced shrub from tropical America and belongs to the Verbena Family. The leaves are oval-shaped and arranged in opposite pairs. The flowers, formed in large numbers from the leaf axils, are pale blue in colour with five fused petals and sepals. There are only four stamens. The ovary gives rise to bright orange berries which stay on the bush for a long time. It is mainly for this attractive feature that the shrub is grown.

After about a kilometre, the forestry road is flanked by trees of *Casuarina*, Chinese Red Pine and Eucalyptus. There are seven species of *Eucalyptus* but probably the most common is the Swamp Mahogany *(E. robusta)* (see photograph on p.123), a tree with dark brown rough bark that grows to a height of about 10 metres. The spirally arranged leaves are thick, dull-green and oval-shaped, tapering to a point. When crushed they give out a strong smell of eucalyptus. These trees are native to Australia and are commonly planted here because they can adapt to a wide range of conditions and are also very fast-growing.

You will also find along the forestry road the Paper-bark Tree *(Melaleuca leucadendron)*, a tall evergreen easily recognised by its many layers of peeling, spongy bark streaked black and white. The spirally arranged, elongate leaves are a dull green and rather thick with up to seven longitudinal veins. When crushed they give out a strong aromatic smell of cajeput oil.

Anywhere along this road, usually in late October or November, you may encounter large swarms of dull brown butterflies with white patches on their wings, probably *Euploea midanus*. They congregate together, often attracted by flowering shrubs such as *Embelia ribes* which bloom at this time of year. These butterflies will soon die as it is the end of the season. They are engaged in a final dance of death, gorging themselves on nectar for a sort of last supper! No one seems to know why they come together in such large numbers. Near Jubilee Reservoir is a place known as Butterfly Valley where the phenomenon occurs every year.

There are a number of paths on the left-hand side of the forestry road. The second, third and fourth of these ascend the hill by means of many well-made steps. Take the fifth to reach the site of Grantham's Camellia. On the way back you will return down the steps of the fourth path where there is a mini reservoir for water storage.

Seen along the forestry road is the Fragrant Litsea *(Litsea cubeba)*, a handsome deciduous tree with simple, alternate leaves. The flowers are unisexual, borne on different trees. At this time of the year the branches bear many green, nodular buds on short stalks, some of which are in the axils of the leaves. Later in the winter the leaves fall and then the bare branches will be seen carrying only the green buds which open in early spring. The yellow male flowers are more showy than the female ones which contain only green ovaries.

The Sumac *(Rhus hypoleuca)* is a deciduous tree growing to a height of about 8 metres with an umbrella-like crown. It has large, alternate, pinnately compound leaves. There are seven to fifteen leaflets arranged in pairs with a single leaflet at the end. The lowest pair of leaflets is the smallest and they increase in size up to the fifth and sixth pairs which are the largest. The seventh pair and the terminal leaflet are smaller than the preceding ones. The leaflets are pointed with toothed margins, and are minutely hairy below. The specific epithet *hypoleuca* refers to the white appearance of the under-side of the leaf, a characteristic not found in either of the two other local species of Rhus. The flowers are borne in large terminal inflorescences in September and may be unisexual and on different trees, although bisexual flowers also occur, sometimes on the same tree with them. The fruits are small, one-seeded, hairy and red in colour. The sap of the Sumac tree may cause intense skin irritation to those who are susceptible.

The Ivy Tree *(Schefflera octophylla)* (see photograph on p. 123) is very common everywhere in Hong Kong. It grows quickly and prefers a sheltered position with good soil. The tree has a smooth, brown bark and its wood is used to make matches. The divided leaves are long-stalked and the leaflets arranged like the fingers of a hand attached to the leaf-stalk at one point. There are six to eight leaflets, hence the specific epithet *octophylla*. Clusters of small white flowers appear from November to December, often attracting butterflies and other insects. The fruit is a small, dark purple berry containing six to eight seeds.

There are many herbaceous plants at the edge of the road. Those that are in bloom are mostly members of the Daisy Family (Compositae) such as *Ageratum conyzoides* with blue flower-heads in terminal cymose clusters and *Inula cappa* with yellow flower-heads in racemose groups. Two species of *Blumea* occur: *B. lacera*, an erect plant, and *B. megacephala*, a scrambling plant with pendulous branches. Both have yellow tubular florets in the flower-heads, lacking the strap-shaped ones as in a Daisy. Another Composite is *Elephantopus tomentosa* which is about 63 cms high when flowering and has a rosette of five or six simple leaves with toothed margins arising close to the base of the stem. The main stem becomes a branched inflorescence bearing leafy bracts in the axils of which are single flower-heads or branches bearing flower-heads. Each

Elecampane
Inula cappa

head actually consists of several in a cluster surrounded by two or three broad, pointed leaf-like bracts. The individual flowers are small and white. The whole plant is very hairy and feels rough to the touch.

Among the herbs occurring frequently along the forest road is the Sword Grass *(Miscanthus floridulus)*. Creepers include: Kudzu Vine *(Pueraria lobata)* belonging to the Pea Family, with leaves occurring singly on weak, climbing stems; *Mikania guaco*; and a scrambling plant, *Rubus reflexus*.

Soon after the fourth path on the left you come to a picnic area on the right of the road where there are some unusually tall *Acacia confusa* trees. On the bank opposite the picnic area is a little colony of *Polytrichum* moss. This moss likes a damp spot. The stems are covered with tiny spirally-arranged leaves of a rich dark green colour.

The forestry road makes a hairpin bend around the hillside where it crosses a stream. After the bend, on the left, is a cement path gently sloping upwards. Take this, the fifth path on your left along the forestry road. You will notice a high bank on your right covered with the hanging fronds of *Blechnum orientale*, the False Staghorn Fern and Sword Grass. Growing along the cement path is Tiger-grass *(Thysanolaena maxima)*. It has tufted, solid stems up to 4 metres tall with broad, stiff leaves with long-pointed tips. The inflorescence is 60 or more cms long, with many slender, oblique branches and branchlets of a purplish colour.

After about a half a kilometre the

Elephantopus tomentosa

cement path becomes a natural track. It runs through woodland for some way, crossing one or two streams and here and there allowing a glimpse of Jubilee Reservoir through the trees. Above the path the hillside slopes up to Tai Mo Shan and is mainly covered by Chinese Red Pine *(Pinus massoniana)*. Below the path the woodland is more mixed. Probably trees of the genus *Machilus* are the most common; at least three of the eight species found in Hong Kong occur here. One is *M. breviflora*, with paired, simple, evergreen leaves. The leaf tip is pointed and the leaf-blade tapers towards the base. The leaves are shiny above, but dull green underneath, and are fairly thick and leathery. The terminal buds are thick and pointed, covered with many bud scales. *M. breviflora* forms a single black fruit that contains juice and a single, black seed.

Three of the eight species of Litsea are present in these woods. Apart from *L. cubeba*, you also see Pond Spice *(L. glutinosa)* and the Round-leaved Litsea *(L. rotundifolia)*. *L. glutinosa* is an evergreen tree about 10 metres high, the young parts of which are softly hairy. The leaves are simple, spirally arranged and oval-shaped, smooth on the upper surface but covered with minute hairs underneath. In early summer small, greenish-yellow flowers are produced in umbrella-like clusters in the leaf axils near the branch ends. The name *glutinosa* comes from the sticky fluid produced when soaking thin slices of the wood in water. This sticky substance was used by village women to dress their hair. *L. rotundifolia* is similar in size to *L. glutinosa* but has smaller leaves with large pointed buds in their axils. The upper surface is dark green, while the lower surface looks whitish. Both *Machilus* and *Litsea* belong to the Laurel Family, which is well represented in Hong Kong.

Two species of Fig *(Ficus)* can be identified in the wood: the Common Yellow-stem Fig *(F. fistulosa)* and the Hairy Mountain Fig *(F. hirta)*. The genus *Ficus* is very common in Hong Kong; twenty-two local species are listed in the *Hong Kong Check List*, and there are probably many more. *F. fistulosa* has alternate, simple leaves blunt at the tip, smooth and hairless. The round- to pear-shaped figs are borne in clusters of three or more on the trunk. *F. hirta* can be recognised by its rough and hairy stems and leaves. The leaves are very variable in shape, the same branch often bearing three distinct types. There are simple leaves, more or less oval-shaped, while others are three- or five-lobed. Rust-coloured hairy figs are borne in the leaf axils.

The only two species of *Abarema* in Hong Kong are present in these woods: Monkeypod *(A. clypearia)* (see photograph on p. 123) and Chinese Apes-earring *(A. lucida)*, both large trees with bipinnately compound leaves. The Monkeypod tree has more leaflets than the Chinese Apes-earring, as many as nine pairs, each divided into three to twelve pairs of pinnules, the larger leaflets being ter-

minal. In autumn the rather curious fruits of Monkeypod may be present. The fruit is a pod coiled into a spiral of two to three rounds. When it splits open the black seeds hang from it on threads, hence the name Monkeypod.

After following the path through the trees for a while you come to a fork. Take the path on your left. This continues for a short distance through the woods before you meet another fork; again take the left one. This path leaves the woods behind and ascends steeply up the hillside, even-

Hairy Mountain Fig
Ficus hirta

tually joining a contour path. On either side of this steep path are small trees, shrubs and grasses. The common shrubs include Rose Myrtle (Rhodomyrtus tomentosa) and Melastoma sanguineum. Among the small trees seen here is Viburnum sempervirens, a member of the Family Caprifoliaceae to which the Honeysuckle and the Elder belong. It has paired, simple leaves appearing to form two rows on the stem, though they are placed at right angles from one pair to the next close to the apex. The leaf-stalks and axillary buds are reddish.

Also seen here are the Wild Cherry (Prunus phaeosticta) of the Family Rosaceae and Rapanea neriifolia of the Family Myrsinaceae. Wild Cherry has alternate simple leaves and prominent, pointed axillary buds. R. neriifolia has simple, elongate leaves forming a close spiral on the stem.

At the beginning of the steep path is a good specimen of Castanopsis fissa. This evergreen tree has large, alternate, simple leaves with serrate margins. There are rust-brown scales on the lower leaf surface. In autumn the tree produces green fruits that split open to set free shiny brown nuts. You will find many of these on the ground under the tree in October and November.

About half-way up the path is the Mountain Fig (Ficus variolosa). This differs from the others found in the woods in that the figs are reddish-brown and are formed in the leaf axils. They look attractive but are not very good to eat. The leaves are simple and spirally arranged. Further up

the path are one or two trees of the Mountain Tallow (Sapium discolor), easily recognised at this time of the year because its leaves have turned red. They do not all fall, however, the tree not being truly deciduous. The leaves are spiral and oval-shaped. In early summer the spikes of small, simple flowers stick up from the branches like candles on a Christmas tree. Male flowers are in the upper part of the spike, with the female ones lower down. The fruit is a black capsule that splits open to shed two black seeds.

Several shrubs bearing clusters of bright red berries are seen on the path. Notable among these is Chloranthus glaber, not more than one metre high, with paired, simple, oblong leaves with serrate edges. The berries are not edible. The Downy Holly (Ilex pubescens) is a much larger shrub. Parts of the plant are hairy, particularly the under-side of the leaves. The simple, oval leaves are arranged alternately. On the stem, below the leaves, are dense clusters of small red berries which appear in October and November. This shrub is quite common in wooded areas at high altitudes.

Twelve species of Ilex are listed in the Hong Kong Check List in the Family Aquifoliaceae, and many of them form berries. Ilex triflora, variety viridis, is also found on the path. At this time of the year it bears green berries in groups of three. The berries are borne in the leaf axils. The simple leaves are alternately arranged and have toothed margins.

Follow the contour path to the right of the steep uphill path. It winds

Downy Holly
Ilex pubescens

up and down as it follows the hillside, keeping at more or less the same level and crossing at least two small streams. Usually *Chirita sinensis* can be seen in bloom at the side of these streams. This low-growing herb flowers most of the year. It has simple, opposite, hairy leaves, all arising from the base of the plant. The flowers are formed in groups of two to six (occasionally singly) at the end of a hairy stalk. Each flower has five short, joined sepals, five petals joined to form a two-lipped bell-shaped tube, four stamens (only two of which are fertile) borne on the corolla tube (the tube formed by the petals of one flower) and a one-celled ovary with a lobed stigma where the pollen is received. The corolla is a pretty shade of lilac and turns sideways in a nodding posture. This delicate herb requires plenty of shade and moist air. It seeks out mountain ravines and nullahs, where it thrives.

After walking for about fifteen minutes on the contour path you will come to a large stream that flows down the south-eastern slopes of Tai Mo Shan. It is on the banks of this stream that *Camellia granthamiana* grows (see photograph on p. 123). To reach it you will have to struggle up the stream about 50 metres from where you joined it, clambering over giant boulders on the stream bed. Keep to the left side of the stream at the beginning where there is a sort of path. This soon disappears, however. A single specimen of Grantham's Camellia is on the right-hand side of the stream as you go up. It is a small tree, about 4-5 metres tall, and has a basal portion nearly half a metre in diameter that gives rise to six or seven much smaller trunks. This form of growth suggests that at some time the tree has been damaged or cut back. The tree is evergreen with simple, glossy, alternate leaves.

The best way of finding Grantham's Camellia is to look for a tree with large white flowers that appear in October and November. The flowers are solitary, without stalks, and formed at the ends of branches. The tree may be covered by flowers at this time, but not densely so. Each flower is surrounded by sepal-like bracts which grade into sepals and are not really distinguishable from them. There are twelve or more of these brown, leathery structures, followed by eight free white petals enclosing a mass of yellow stamens in the centre. This Camellia is very special because its flowers are 14 cms across, making them the largest in the world. It was discovered in 1955 but it was only some years later that other specimens were found, a few close by on Tai Mo Shan, and some on Ma On Shan.

The ovary of Grantham's Camellia is above the stamens, petals and floral leaves. The style is straight and there are five stigmatic branches to receive pollen. There are five chambers with one or two seeds in each chamber. The fruit is a large brown woody capsule which splits into five valves to set the seeds free. Each seed is about the size of a broad bean. The seeds only germinate with difficulty, so vegetative methods of propagation have been used to obtain plants for cultivation.

Having bid farewell to Grantham's Camellia, retrace your steps down the stream and return along the contour path that you came up on. There is no need to go back exactly the same way. Carry on along the contour path. You will be well rewarded, for the views from this path are excellent, both of the Kowloon Hills and Lion Rock, as well as of Hong Kong Island. At one point you will come to a hill crest, and there all Hong Kong is spread below you. In the late afternoon the sun will be setting over the sea in the west turning everything to gold. There are even golden flowers, for the creeper *Gelsemium elegans* grows along the path. It forms dense yellow clusters of fragrant flowers borne at the branch ends. The plant is a woody climber with twisting stems, and has paired, simple leaves that are shiny and hairless. But beware! This plant is one of the most poisonous in Hong Kong. Three leaves, if eaten, could kill you.

Finally you will descend what seems like a million steps to the forestry road below.

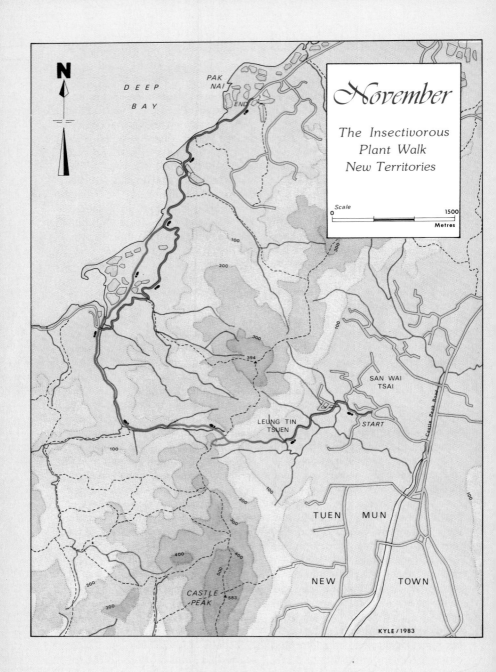

N

DEEP
BAY

PAK
NAI
END

November

The Insectivorous
Plant Walk
New Territories

Scale
0   1500
Metres

100

200

300

100

394

300

SAN WAI
TSAI

Castle Peak Road

LEUNG TIN
TSUEN

START

100

100

100

TUEN   MUN

200

300

400

500

NEW   TOWN

200

CASTLE
PEAK

583

300

KYLE/1983

November

The Insectivorous Plant Walk
Castle Peak, New Territories
Time: 5 — 6 Hours

The route in brief

Among Hong Kong's insectivorous plants — plants that attract and trap insects — is the Pitcher Plant which thrives among the banks of streams in a shallow valley near Tuen Mun in the New Territories. To see it, head for the Castle Peak Mental Hospital. Take the road leading from the hospital in a westerly direction between houses. Follow a right fork near the start and a little later a left fork. The road winds, but keep straight on, ignoring any turnings on your right. At first there are houses but eventually you reach a rural area. The road now runs parallel with the Castle Peak range of mountains, passing through a banana plantation. Near the end of this take an obvious right fork that climbs up through trees. Follow it under some electric power lines until you cross a firing range (not in use on Sundays and public holidays). The right fork climbs steeply through open hillside towards Castle Peak.

About three-quarters of the way up take a left fork. When you reach the top of the hill turn right along a path that leads to a shallow valley where the Pitcher Plant grows. Take the path that follows the stream down this valley in a westerly direction. The path crosses the stream from the left to the right bank. A tributary joins the stream from the right; cross over. The path follows the valley and the stream, and lower down you cross over to the left bank. Carry on along the left bank until you reach a bridge. Cross the bridge and follow the road to Pak Nai.

An alternative and more pleasant route takes you over a foot-bridge a little further down the stream. After crossing the stream the path runs through cultivated fields and duck ponds to Pak Nai. From there buses may be taken home.

The Walk

As you walk along the road look out for Purple Camel's Foot *(Bauhinia purpurea)*, a deciduous tree native to Hong Kong which reaches a height of about 17 metres. You will find this tree near the start of the road. The leaves are characteristic of the genus, having a two-lobed appearance, being cleft to about half their length by a notch, just as the foot of a camel is cleft. The flowers, pale purple in colour, with a rather faded look, have a sweet smell. The flower has a tubular calyx split down one side, five free petals and three or four fertile stamens. The ovary develops into a large pod. The pods are very conspicuous on the tree later on in the year and in early spring, and enable one to distinguish this species of Bauhinia from the Hong Kong Orchid Tree *(B. blakeana)*, the floral emblem of Hong Kong which never forms fruits and can only be propagated vegetatively.

Extremely common along the road is the creeper Mile-a-minute *(Mikania guaco)*, a member of the Daisy Family (Compositae). It is rare to have climbing respresentatives in this family. Whole areas quickly become covered with the twisting stems bearing paired, heart-shaped leaves. In November the plants produce masses of small sweet-smelling white flowerheads, each consisting of four tubular florets. These heads are formed in branched inflorescences in the leaf axils.

Two climbing plants of the family Convolvulaceae which occur along the road are the Fingerleaf Morning Glory *(Ipomoea digitata)* and the Cardinal Vine *(Quamoclit pennata)*. The leaves of the Fingerleaf Morning Glory are deeply cleft into five to seven narrow finger-like lobes. The leaf-blade is more or less round in shape and has a long stalk. The flowers are trumpet-shaped, pink- or lilac-coloured, darker in the throat and paler on the outer surface. It climbs by the stem twisting around supports. The Cardinal Vine only occurs in the wild as an escaped garden species. The leaves are pinnately compound and the leaflets are thread-like, giving the leaves a spiky appearance. The flowers are bright red with petals that form a long narrow tube expanding in the upper part into five short flat petal lobes. This plant, a worthwhile addition to a balcony 'garden', can be grown easily from seed. Another garden escape you may see along the way is the Four o'clock plant *(Mirabilis jalapa)*, a low

Four o'clock Plant
Mirabilis jalapa

136

shrub with simple, paired leaves and tubular cerise-coloured flowers that emit a strong perfume in the evening (they don't open fully until sundown), and so are most likely pollinated by moths. This plant is in the same family as Bougainvillea.

Towards the end of the banana plantation there is an obvious path on the right-hand side of the road that climbs upwards among the trees. You will find that it crosses a firing range. Red warning flags are put out if the range is in use. Several large grasses growing nearby will be in flower at this time of the year. Ciliate Sasagrass *(Microstegium ciliatum)*, grows in shady spots. The strap-shaped leaves are of a light green colour. The inflorescence is characteristically made up of a number of buff-coloured spikes (from three to eleven in number) that are arranged at different levels on the axis although they tend to be pressed close together, looking like a single spike. Another native grass seen here is the so-called Reed-like Grass *(Neyraudia reynaudiana)*. It is often taller than a man and has a large shiny, brownish densely branched inflorescence. The spikelets look feathery because awns are present. A very large grass found close by is the Sword Grass *(Miscanthus floridulus)*. It can be distinguished from most other grasses in Hong Kong by the unbroken white streak down the middle of the leaf blade. It has a tall inflorescence with a one-sided look because the spikes are arranged in half rings. It is red and shining at first, but later brown and fluffy.

As the path climbs upwards take a right fork, and in the damp places near the stream look for the Common Day-flower *(Commelina communis)* and the Mountain Knotweed *(Polygonum chinense)*. The former is a monocotyledon with bright blue flowers, the latter a bushy, branching herb with pink-tinged stems and leaf stalks, and clusters of small white flowers.

Soon the path takes you into the open hillside. Here the commonest plants are the False Staghorn Fern *(Dicranopteris linearis)* and Dwarf Mountain Pine *(Baeckea frutescens)*, a low shrub covered with many tiny, paired leaves. It looks like a heath plant and is known to many Europeans as Hong Kong Heather. The plant is dotted with glands containing oil, giving it a resinous smell. The flowers are tiny and white, occurring in the axils of the leaves. It is very common on exposed hillsides and likes an acid soil. Along the path the

Dwarf Mountain Pine
Baeckea frutescens

137

grass-like leaves of *Dianella ensifolia*, a member of the Lily Family, can be seen here and there. It is now producing bright purple berries. Two members of the Daisy Family present are the Hairy Bur-Marigold *(Bidens pilosa)* with yellow flower-heads and barbed fruits that stick to animals' coats and enable them to be dispersed, and Iron-weed *(Vernonia cinerea)* with bright purple flower-heads.

Three-quarters of the way up the hill take the right-hand fork. This will take you directly to the source of the stream where the Pitcher Plant grows. The left fork takes you up a little higher. The extra climb may be worth it, for at the top of this path on the crest of the hill the Balloon Flower *(Platycodon grandiflorum)* might be found in bloom. *P. grandiflorum* (see photograph on p. 144), looks like a giant harebell. Sometimes the flow-

Dianella ensifolia

Hairy Bur-Marigold
Bidens pilosa

When mature the pitcher is up to 15 cm long and 4 cm wide, of a pale-green or reddish-green colour. At the upper end, at the mouth of the pitcher, there is a lid to keep the rain out. When the pitcher is young and still developing, this lid is closed, but when the leaf is fully grown the lid opens to expose the cavity inside. The pitcher's inner wall is lined with glands. In the upper part they secrete a sugary fluid like nectar, which attracts insects. In the lower part the glands secrete a fluid containing protein-digesting enzymes, so the base of the pitcher contains a pool of digestive liquid.

Insects, attracted by the sugary secretions and extra-floral nectaries, alight on the rim of the pitcher mouth. Because it curves inward and is slippery, the insects fall into the fluid at the bottom of the pitcher. Escape is impossible because the walls of the pitcher are too slippery and there is a ring of hairs near the top pointing downwards to prevent further passage. The trapped insects soon drown and the soft parts of their bodies are digested by the enzymes in the pool. The products of digestion are absorbed by the cells lining the walls of the lower part of the pitcher (possibly by the digestive glands only). The solid parts cannot be digested and cannot be got rid of in any other way, so in time the pitchers become filled with the dead insects' remains — a black and yellow striped wasp is particularly common. By this time the pitchers have probably become non-functional and various creatures may be found living in them, such as mosquito larvae. In Malaysia a species of

ers, aster-violet in colour, are borne singly, but often in a small candelabra of eight to ten. The parts of the flower are in rings of five. They are a lovely sight. The unopened flower buds have an unusual charm as they are inflated, looking like Chinese lanterns turned sideways. It flowers from August to the end of the year.

Find the shallow valley where there is a stream running towards the west, away from the direction of Tuen Mun. Growing along the banks of the stream is the Hong Kong Pitcher Plant *(Nepenthes mirabilis)* (see photograph on p. 144) with green pitcher-like leaves, the older ones spotted with dark red. This is a sprawling plant but it can climb too, holding on to supports with the twisting tendrillar portions of its leaves. The leaves, alternately arranged on the stems, are interesting. The midrib of the leaf-blade is extended to form a tendril, which bears the pitcher at its tip.

tree frog breeds in the pitchers.

Some of the Pitcher Plants may still be flowering. The dark red flowers are formed in tall racemes about one metre high. Plants are either male or female. Male flowers have a knob-like group of about twelve fused stamens (sometimes more or less) at the end of a short column. Female flowers have single, greenish-coloured ovaries with four chambers. Both male and female flowers have four dark red sepals; petals are absent. Many tall spikes of the fruits will be seen. The fruit is an elongated, brown capsule that splits four ways. Many seeds occur in one capsule. As they are very light they are dispersed by wind.

The Sundew (*Drosera* species) is very common in the area round the source of the stream. Here the soil is very wet, just the sort of habitat it likes. There are so many of the reddish, rosette-like plants that they form a continuous carpet. The upper surface of the small rounded or oval leaves is covered with long, sticky glandular appendages called tentacles, usually red in colour and particularly abundant on the leaf margin. The heads of the tentacles secrete a sticky substance that attracts and traps small insects which alight on them. The tentacles are fairly sensitive, and a contact stimulus is felt by all the tentacles in that neighbourhood of the leaf, so that they bend over towards the prey and attach themselves to it. The insect is thus pressed onto the surface of the leaf. The glandular tentacle heads secrete a protein-digesting enzyme which digests the soft parts of the insect's body. When all that can be broken down from the insect's body has been absorbed by the tentacles, they move back and the indigestible remains blow away.

The two species of *Drosera* present here are *D. burmanni*, which has short broad spoon-shaped leaves, and *D. spathulata* with much longer leaves shaped like a spatula. The length of the leaf stalk is twice that of *D. burmanni*. *D. burmanni* bears white flowers in May, while *D. spathulata* produces pink flowers in April. The inflorescence is a one-sided cyme of up to ten flowers. The fruit is a capsule opening by three longitudinal slits.

Growing among the *Drosera* is a sedge called the Chinese Scaly Seed (*Lepidosperma chinense*). It covers a large area near the stream, and appears to like wet conditions. It is a curious plant, since the above-ground portion consists only of a green stem without leaves. It is this stem that carries out photosynthesis, the manufacture of sugar from carbon dioxide and water under the influence of sunlight. In most other plants photosynthesis takes place mainly in the leaves. The stem is flat on one side and rounded on the other, not three-sided as in most sedges. Some of the stems terminate in a spike of spikelets, very similar to those of grasses. The minute details of the spikelets, however, are different. The masses of spiky stems give the plant a rush-like appearance. True rushes occur in another family, the Juncaceae.

Follow the path that runs close to the stream and down the valley in a westerly direction. Here and there you cross the stream, but there are always boulders you can use as stepping stones. The path is generally quite good though rough. Towards the lower reaches of the stream considerable erosion has occurred, and in a few places the path is broken by deep cuttings, but you can always clamber round. Pitcher plants occur all along the stream wherever it is damp. In the valley there is a small tributary that comes in from the right as you go down, and later one from the left.

Vegetation in this valley is fairly sparse; erosion and lack of soil have prevented any large trees becoming established. However there are several Chinese Red Pines (Pinus massoniana). Another fairly common native tree is Acronychia pedunculata, a member of the Rutaceae Family containing the genus Citrus, that includes the tangerine, lemon, pomelo, etc. This small tree has a dense crown of foliage and slender branches. The leaves are simple, tapering at both ends. When crushed they give off a strong, resinous smell. At this time of the year the tree is recognized by the round, greenish-yellow fruits that hang from the leaf axils. They are edible and sweet-tasting but not very juicy as there is a large, single seed inside.

Another small native tree found here is the False Camellia (Gordonia axillaris) (see photograph on p. 144), producing large, white flowers in winter with a mass of bright yellow stamens in the centre. The fruit is a woody capsule. Many such capsules can be seen on the trees at this time, and some may still contain a few of the characteristic winged seeds. This latter feature distinguishes the plant from the genus Camellia. Among several large shrubs common in this valley is the Chinese Buttonbush (Adina pilulifera). Slender and much-branched, it reaches a height of about 3 metres. The simple leaves are in opposite pairs, tapering at both ends. Small white flowers borne in globular heads are formed in summer, and by this time of the year they have given rise to a similar shaped collection of small fruits. The latter split into two valves to allow the escape of the small, winged seeds.

Another shrub is the Hong Kong Hawthorn (Rhaphiolepis indica) whose pale pink or white flowers that appear in early spring resemble the European hawthorn. At this time of the year it bears clusters of small, rounded, bluish-black berries. False Tea (Eurya chinensis) also forms black berries. It is common all along the

Acronychia
Acronychia pedunculata

stream. Like Gordonia it belongs to the Camellia (Theaceae) Family. At this time of the year many tiny, green flower buds can be seen among the leaves. The flowers open in December and are white, either male or female. They occur on different plants, so the sexes are distinguishable, not a very common feature among plants. *Wickstroemia indica* is also found, especially at the lower end of the valley. A shrub with opposite, simple leaves, its flowers are greenish-yellow, followed by berries which are at first green and later red. In Chinese herbal medicine the leafy shoots are used as an antidote for snake bite. The berries are poisonous.

There are only a few herbaceous plants in this eroded valley, the most common occurring at the side of the stream. It is surprisingly an orchid, the Bamboo Orchid *(Arundina chinensis)* (see photograph on p. 144). This plant likes a position in full sun, and grows along the edge of the stream in great leafy, often trailing tufts, looking somewhat like bamboo. The leaves are grass-like, growing in two ranks all the way up the stem, with pointed tips. The typical orchid flower is a delightful shade of rose-pink, two to eight of them forming a raceme. The flower parts are in threes, with a yellow centre and a deep red-purple lip. The fruit is an elongate capsule that splits three ways to set free the tiny, dust-like seeds. It flowers from August to November so you should see plenty of blooms.

Several climbers of interest occur in this valley, notably the Sandpaper Vine *(Tetracera scandens (L) Merr.)*, a woody climber whose leaves are very rough. The leaves are broad, bluntly pointed and usually toothed. The plant commences growth as a woody shrub but soon the stem tips twist around supports and become climbing shoots. The white flowers are small and fragrant. The white ovary changes as it ripens into a red, hairy fruit with a short beak. It is a very common native plant of Hong Kong.

The Creeping Psychotria *(Psychotria serpens)* may be seen crawling over rocks or on the trunks of trees to which it adheres by means of its sticky, adventitious roots. The oval leaves occur in pairs, often flattened against the surface on which the plant is climbing. There are stipules between the leaves at first, but they soon fall and leave a scar which can only be detected easily with a hand lens. The scarring between the leafstalks is a characteristic of the Family Rubiaceae to which it belongs. In November the Creeping Psychotria often bears terminal clusters of white berries sometimes likened to Mistletoe. But the berries of the Mistletoe are translucent while those of *P. serpens* are quite opaque.

At least three species of Greenbrier *(Smilax)* occur. All have characteristic paired tendrils for climbing, joined to the base of the leaf and therefore regarded as modified stipules by botanists. The most common is China Root *(Smilax glabra)*, often completely covering the bush over which it is climbing. The lance-shaped alternate leaves are dark green above but light green below and quite hairless. (The name *glabra* refers to the lack of hairs.) The Long-leaved Greenbrier (*Smilax corbularia*) has similar shaped leaves but the under-surface is glaucus — white with a bluish sheen. *S. china* has much broader leaves. The flowers of *Smilax* are greenish, formed in umbels in the leaf axils; male and female flowers occur on separate plants. The fruits of *S. glabra* are green at first, later bluish-black while *S. china* has bright red berries, ripe in October.

As one descends the valley the stream becomes wider and deeper and the banks spread out. Finally you come to a road bridge on your right (you are now on the left bank) that crosses the stream. You can take this bridge and follow the road to Pak Nai, about 6 kilometres or about an hour's walk, or you can take the next bridge a bit further down. This one is a footbridge that leads to a pleasant path running through some areas of cultivation. This is the more interesting route.

At length you get to Pak Nai where small stalls sell drinks and where you can rest before journeying home.

Long-leaved Greenbrier (male plant)
Smilax corbularia

143

Bamboo Orchid
Arundina chinensis

Hong Kong Pitcher Plant
Nepenthes mirabilis

False Camellia
Gordonia axillaris

Balloon Flower
Platycodon grandiflorum

Schima
Schima superba

Chloranthus glaber

Oriental Blechnum
Blechnum orientale

Green Alga
Trentepohlia

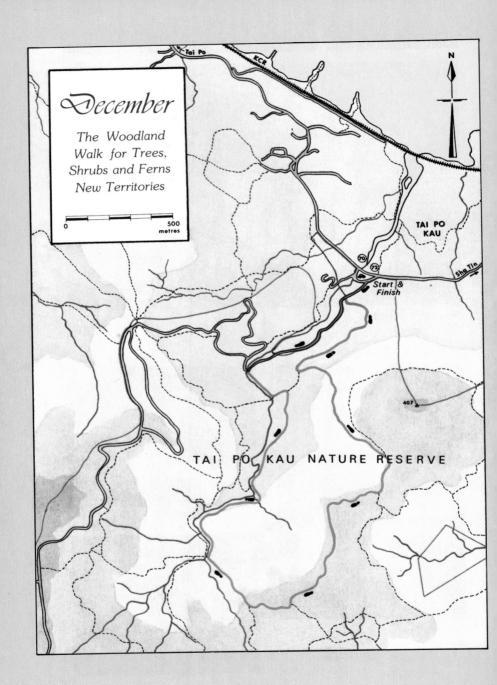

December

The Woodland
Walk for Trees,
Shrubs and Ferns
New Territories

0   500
     metres

N

Tai Po

KCR

TAI PO
KAU

70
73

Sha Tin

Start &
Finish

407

TAI PO KAU NATURE RESERVE

December

The Woodland Walk for Trees, Shrubs and Ferns
Tai Po Kau Forest,
New Territories
Time: 3 — 4 hours

The route in brief

S everal thousand years of man's activities have severely restricted the forest areas, many of which have been replaced by scrubland or grassland. A typical Hong Kong forest is described as evergreen oak or semideciduous. This walk, through the Tai Po Kau Forest, is a saunter through the woodland to see Hong Kong's trees, shrubs and ferns.

Travel along the Tai Po Road towards Sha Tin. About 2 kilometres out of Tai Po, near a car park and a picnic area under the trees, you will see two forestry roads. When facing them take the left road. Follow this road for about five minutes until you come to a path on your left. Take the steps upwards. This path goes through woodland. When you come to a T-junction, turn left in the direction of the yellow and brown arrows. After a while there is a left turn marked by yellow arrows. Ignore this and continue on the path marked with brown arrows. At length there is another T-junction. Turn right down a steep path, leaving the 'brown walk', until you come to a stream with a path running alongside it marked with blue arrows. Turn on to this path and go against the arrows. After a while you reach a slanting T-junction. Keep right and continue on the 'red and blue walk' against the arrows. After passing through a picnic area and a turning on the right, which is the beginning of the yellow and brown walks, you will eventually join the forestry road that leads you back to the point where you started the walk.

The Walk

Almost immediately on your right as you enter the forestry road is the Wood-oil Tree *(Aleurites montana)*, 10 metres tall and easily recognised by its large palmately lobed leaves with long petioles. There are normally two curious cup-like glands at the base of the lamina which function as extra-floral nectaries to attract insect pollinators. The tree sheds its leaves in winter, but in December it may still be in full leaf. In April it produces clusters of white, showy flowers which contain either stamens, usually ten in number, on male trees or an ovary on female trees. The egg-shaped fruit has oil-containing seeds.

Near to the Wood-oil Tree, on the same side, are several Rose-apple *(Syzygium jambos)* trees. These may be flowering in late December but they are usually not in bloom until January. Further along the road, still on the right, are some Sweet Gum trees *(Liquidambar formosana)* about 30 metres or more high. Although deciduous, some leaves may still be on the branches. The lamina has a characteristic shape, with three distinct pointed lobes, like a Maple leaf. The leaf margin is serrate. The flowers are unisexual, the small males being in catkin-like racemes, the females in globose heads, borne on the same tree.

The fruit, a spiny spherical structure, is made up of many capsules with small winged seeds for wind dispersal. The spiny appearance is due to styles of the ovaries that stick outwards from the group.

There is an interesting dead tree on your right at the beginning of the forestry road. It is covered with the growth of two epiphytic ferns (an epiphytic plant is one that grows on, but is not fed by, another plant): the Tongue Fern *(Pyrrosia adnascens)* and *Lemmaphyllum microphyllum*, which look similar but can be distinguished by the shape of their sterile fronds. In *P. adnascens* they are elliptical while in *L. microphyllum* they are rounded. *P. adnascens'* long creeping rhizome, bearing both sterile and fertile fronds, fixes itself to bark and rocks by its adventitious roots. The sterile fronds are elliptical with a rounded apex. The fertile fronds are much longer and more or less linear, the upper half covered on the underside with brown sporangia. *L. microphyllum* also has a long creeping rhizome and both sterile and fertile fronds. The sterile fronds are irregularly rounded in shape and rather fleshy; the fertile fronds are practically club-shaped, with sporangia forming an oval group on each side of the midrib in the upper half on the underside.

There are big clumps of *Blechnum orientale* Fern (see photograph on p. 145) along the left bank, and False Staghorn Fern *(Dicranopteris linearis)*. These are common throughout the Tai Po Kau Forest Reserve. At this time of year, they might be seen uncoiling their new leaves. The Climbing Fern *(Lygodium japonicum)* can be seen struggling up any suitable support. Another species of *Lygodium, L. microphyllum (Cav) R. Br.*, synonym *L. scandens Smartz*, is present. It is more delicate than the first species mentioned and the forked leaflets along the midrib are divided only once, never twice as is common in *L. japonicum*. The midribs of the leaf climb by anti-clockwise twisting.

Three of the nine species of the genus *Pteris* in Hong Kong are seen on the bank of the forestry road. These are *P. semipinnata*, *P. vittata* and *P. ensiformis*. *P. semipinnata* and *P. ensiformis* typically occur on earthy banks in fairly shady positions, while *P. vittata* can be found in more open situations among rocks and is often found growing in wall crevices. All share a characteristic common to the genus: they all have marginal sporangia. *P. vittata* has large sterile fronds that are divided once, and leaflets with a pointed tip, the basal leaflets usually being the smallest. In the twice-divided and smaller sterile fronds of *P. ensiformis* there are one to four pairs of opposite leaflets, each being deeply lobed or divided into pinnules, of a rounded shape with serrate margins and an

elongated tip. The fertile fronds of *P. vittata* are similar in appearance to the sterile fronds, the sporangia being borne along the margins of the leaflets, not quite reaching the base or the tip. The margin is reflexed to form a protective cover (indusium). In *P. ensiformis* the fertile fronds are much larger than the sterile ones and the leaflets much narrower. The fertile lamina is nearly twice the length of the sterile lamina, and has two to three pairs of narrow lateral leaflets and an elongate terminal leaflet. The sporangia are similar to those of *P. vittata*.

After you have been walking up the forestry road for about five minutes take a path with steps to your left. It leads through woodland and follows a delightful route. If it is late December, you may come upon the splendid site of a male tree of the Fragrant Litsea *(Litsea cubeba)* in full bloom. As the tree is deciduous, the profusion of creamy yellow flowers clothes the bare branches.

Pteris ensiformis
(left: fertile frond,
right: sterile frond)

Pteris vittata
(fertile frond)

Several Mountain Tallow Trees (*Sapium discolor*) along the woodland path are seen displaying bright red leaves. Soon the autumnal leaves will fall off, but in December they are usually still crowning the tree with glory. You are passing through a woodland of mixed trees. There are a few *Pinus massoniana*, *Castanopsis fissa*, *Schefflera octophylla* and Monkeypod (*Abarema clypearia*). China Fir Trees (*Cunninghamia lanceolata*) are scattered here and there as are two species of fig — *Ficus hirta* and *Ficus fistulosa*.

At one point along the path you will come across a large tree of *Sterculia lanceolata* bearing the Forestry Department label. Another tree common to these woods is *Schima superba*, a large, fine tree with simple, alternate leaves of lanceolate shape (see photograph on p. 145). From May to July it produces large numbers of white, Camellia-like flowers that completely cover the tree. If you look down on the forest from a vantage point during the flowering season, the individual trees may be seen as white blobs dotted here and there among the dark foliage of other trees. The flowers occur in the leaf axils or as terminal racemose groups. There are five free sepals, five almost free petals, numerous stamens and a superior five-celled ovary. The fruit is a woody capsule.

Further along you will come to a tree stump covered with a growth of *Pyrrosia lingua*, another species of the Tongue Fern similar to the one seen earlier. It differs from *P. adnascens* in that the fertile and sterile fronds are the same size, both of lan-

ceolate shape. The sporangia often cover the whole of the under-surface of the fertile frond, whereas in *P. adnascens* they only cover the upper half. It may also be seen growing over the surface of rocks.

In lighter parts of the wood at the side of the path some attractive herbs may be seen. The Creeping Melastoma (*Melastoma dodecandrum*) forms a carpet in places and even shows its pink flowers. *Dianella ensifolia*, with its purple fruits, may also be present, together with Lily Turf (*Liriope spicata*) which has tufted grass-like leaves and black berries.

Moneywort (*Centella asiatica*), a creeping herb widely used in Chinese medicine, occurs all along the path. It forms roots at the point on the horizontal stems where the leaves arise. The kidney-shaped leaves with long petioles have crenulate margins of small rounded lobes that are not pointed. The tiny white flowers are in umbels and the fruit is a small, globose capsule. This plant is used by the Chinese to cure hepatitis, the common cold and snake bites. It is also applied externally to stop the bleeding of wounds.

At least sixteen species of shrubs are seen on this walk. Three of these — *Melodinus suaveolens*, *Tetracera scandens*, and *Mussaenda pubescens* — become high climbers. Probably the most common in these woods are *Daphniphyllum calycinum*, *Psychotria rubra* and *Eurya chinensis*. All three species occur in scrubland too, suggesting the overlapping nature of plant communities in Hong Kong. Other shrubs include *Embelia laeta*, *Glochidion eriocarpum*, *Melastoma sanguineum*, and *Pandanus furcatus*.

Chloranthus glaber (see photograph on p. 145) is one of the most striking shrubs, with its bright red berries and shiny opposite toothed leaves. *Dalbergia benthami*, a straggling shrub, and *Embelia ribes*, a shrub of similar habit whose flowers attract butterflies, are both present. The remaining three shrubs seen are *Justicia ventricosa*, *Rourea microphylla* and *Saurauia tristyla*. The division of plants into three layers according to their size, namely herbs, shrubs and trees, is very evident in these woods. Botanists call this stratification.

After following the path for about three quarters of an hour you come to one that crosses it. Follow the yellow and brown arrows pointing to the left. At this junction is a large specimen of the Ivy Tree. This may be in full bloom with swarms of bees on the small, yellow flowers. A bare tree of *Sapium discolor* may also be seen, its trunk covered with the

Rourea microphylla

Saurauia tristyla

Creeping Psychotria bearing bunches of white berries. As you wander along the woodland path, after making the left turn, you should see Sweet Gum *(Liquidambar formosana)*, Chinese Red Pine and Fragrant Litsea.

Deeper in the woods there is an abundance of *Machilus* species, particularly the Red Machilus *(M. thunbergii)*. An evergreen tree, *M. thunbergii* has spiral, lanceolate, leathery, bluntly pointed leaves with a bluish-white (glaucus) sheen beneath. The leaf arrangement is variable, sometimes appearing to be opposite and not spiral. The terminal winter buds are covered by many overlapping scales which leave clearly marked scars on the branches after falling. Large terminal buds in winter and limp, reddish young leaves in early spring are typical of most species of *Machilus*. The leaf size and shape is rather variable even within the same species, which does not help identification. Flowers, formed in panicles, appear with the leaves at the branch

151

Red Machilus Tree
Machilus thunbergii

tips in spring. Each flower has a perianth (this includes the sepals and petals) of two whorls of three greenish segments. There are nine stamens in whorls of three and a single ovary in the centre of the flower. The fruit is a globose black berry. *M. thunbergii* is in the Family Lauraceae, which also includes the genus Litsea and, surprisingly, the semiparasitic climber *Cassytha filiformis*.

Evodia lepta of the Family Rutaceae to which citrus trees belong, is a much smaller tree recognisable by its opposite, trifoliate leaves. Of the three leaflets that form the lamina, the middle one is the largest. Axillary cymes of small yellowish-white flowers are formed in spring. The fruit is a capsule. Also in the Family Rutaceae is the genus *Zanthoxylum* which are small trees or shrubs that have pinnately compound, prickly leaves. One of these, the Prickly Ash *(Z. avicennae)*, is found in the Tai Po Kau woods. The leaves are spirally arranged and once-pinnate with many leaflets forming two rows, one on either side of the midrib. The stems, petioles and midribs are very prickly. This small tree may also be recognised by the toothed bark that it forms.

The tree that probably gave Hong Kong its name 'Fragrant Harbour' is the Joss Stick Tree *(Aquilaria sinensis)*. Quite common in this part of the woods, this small (not much more than 5 metres tall) tree has alternate, simple, ovate leaves. It used to be much cultivated in the area of Hong Kong harbour, when its scented wood was used for making joss sticks and fans. The strongly scented flowers are small and greenish-yellow, formed in clusters at the ends of branches and in the leaf axils. The fruit, an egg-shaped capsule densely covered with short, grey hairs, contains black seeds.

Two other common trees are the Round-leaved Litsea *(Litsea rotundifolia)* and *Aporusa chinensis*. A species of *Quercus* also seen in the earlier part of the walk is present

Joss Stick Tree
Aquilaria sinensis

152

along this path as well as *Schima superba*, both of which are common throughout the Tai Po Kau forest. *Symplocos laurina (Retz.) Wall*, synonym *Symplocos cochinchinensis (Retz.) Noot.*, occurs too. It is a tree with spiral, simple leaves of broadly elliptic shape with a crenulate margin. It flowers in early summer, forming a branched spike in the leaf axils. Many small white flowers occur, with five sepals, the same number of petals and many stamens. The single ovary gives rise to a globose fruit that is surrounded by the persistent calyx that gives it a beaked look.

The Stiff-leaved Meliosma *(Meliosma rigida)*, so named because its elongate, simple, spiral leaves are stiff and leathery, has a finely pointed leaf tip with a number of 'teeth'. The rest of the margin, however, is smooth. The leaf base tapers towards the petiole. The under-surface of the leaf is thickly covered with rust-coloured hairs, as are the parts of the inflorescence, a terminal panicle of many small, greenish flowers.

The path you are following is quite rocky. Here and there are large boulders, sometimes covered with a growth of *Pyrrosia lingua*, one of the two Tongue Ferns, or with the Creeping Psychotria. At one point there is a very good view of the reclaimed land around Tai Po. Soon after passing a very large rock you will see a left turn near a stream, signposted with yellow arrows. Ignore this and proceed on the path marked by brown arrows through an area of bamboo. Carry on along the brown arrow path, ignoring a second turning on your left with some earthen steps.

The forest soon becomes more open and there are large areas of Sword Grass *(Miscanthus floridulus)* on either side. In December, its inflorescences are beginning to look fluffy as they commence to ripen and form seed. They have a distinct one-sided look. There are big clumps of the fern *Blechnum orientale* along the path, preferring, it seems, a position with more light than in the dense woods. Now that there are few trees many hillside shrubs occur, such as *Melastoma sanguineum* and Rose Myrtle *(Rhodomyrtus tomentosa)*. Clumps of Black Sedge *(Ghania tristis)*, are also present. This, too, does best in the sun.

The Chinese Red Pine occurs in the open part of the forest, although many have died and become completely covered by growths of the Creeping Psychotria. Many pines in Hong Kong have recently been killed by a nematode (eelworm) disease that is spread by the long-horned beetle, so this may have been the cause. Bacteria on the nematode form a toxin that kills the pine shoots. There are also trees of Fragrant Litsea here, looking very lovely when in full bloom and more *Sapium discolor* with its red leaves.

Ignore another left turn which you will soon see. Shortly you will pass through a glade of *Blechnum orientale* ferns. It is a pleasant spot, and if there were wood fairies, you would probably find them here. About twenty minutes further on, through open woodland, you arrive at a T-junction. A brown arrow pointing to the left up a hill indicates the 'brown walk', while there is a steeply sloping downward path to the right. Take the path to the right.

Just as you approach the T-junction you will be treated to a lovely sight of the Strawberry Tree *(Myrica rubra)* in full bud. The dark red flower buds occur in catkin-like spikes, sticking upwards in the leaf axils to give the whole tree a ruddy, glowing appearance. This small evergreen tree grows to a height of about 5 metres. It is characterised by simple, spiral oval-shaped leaves with rounded tips and smooth leaf margins. The buds usually open in March revealing simple flowers that lack sepals and petals. Male and female flowers appear on different trees. The male flowers are yellow, consisting of six to ten stamens, while the female flowers are greenish, each including a one-celled ovary with a single ovule. The fruit ripens in May as a red, succulent globular structure looking like a

Strawberry Tree
Myrica rubra

strawberry, hence the common name. It has a very sharp, acid flavour, but is popular for making preserves and fruit-drinks.

Take care as you descend the steep path; it can be very slippery in wet weather. But take notice of *Machilus thunbergii, Evodia lepta* and *Zanthoxylum avicennae*. There is a species of *Symplocos* different from *S. laurina* encountered earlier, with smaller leaves, reddish stem and leaf stalks. Some of the *M. thunbergii* trees may show curious club-shaped outgrowths on the leaves, presumably an insect gall of some kind, and shaped very much like the stalk and capsule of a moss. There are also some Camphor trees *(Cinnamomum camphora)*. Common along the descending path is the Sedge *Ghania tristis* and the Sword Grass, showing that there isn't much shade.

You eventually come to the main stream that traverses the central valley of the Tai Po Kau Country Park. Do not cross but follow the path alongside, travelling against the blue arrows and in the direction that the stream flows. It is a pleasant, shady path with little bridges every so often over tributaries and all the time you can hear the trickle of water and the babble of the brook.

Quite soon you will find four medium-sized Paper-bark trees *(Melaleuca leucadendron)* on your right, their white bark standing out against the rest of the vegetation. On your left by the stream, Mountain Orange *(Melodinus suaveolens)* is climbing high on various shrubs and trees and showing off its large orange fruits. A big Camphor tree on your left has a large branch projecting across the path on which the Creeping Psychotria is seen displaying its white berries. Shortly there is a high bank on your right covered by *Gleichenia chinensis*, its forking fronds overhanging the path. This fern is not very common in Hong Kong, although it is also found on Lantau.

An enormous rock on your left is seen to be covered by the growth of a terrestrial Green Alga *(Trentepohlia)* (see photograph on p. 145) which is in fact not green but bright orange. This is because the orange pigments of the alga mask the green colour of the chlorophyll. If you examined the orange growth under a microscope you would see that it is made up of filaments composed of cells joined end to end. The rock is also host to various grey-green lichens composed of a fungus growing in close association with a unicellular green alga for mutual benefit. Such an association is known as symbiosis.

The low-growing shrub *Chloranthus glaber* with its bright red berries is common along the return path, gladdening the eye. There are many ferns here, especially on the bank to your right. After a while you come to a sloping T-junction, where you turn to the right. You are now on the combination path of the red and blue walks, although still walking against the arrows. (The turning on the left is the red walk, a very short one, that crosses the stream.) The path you are on leaves the stream for a while and takes you through a glade of Paper-bark trees to a pleasant picnic area where you can sit at wooden tables in the shade of Brisbane Box.

Continue on from the picnic area against the red and blue arrows and soon you will see a path on your right. Ignore this. It is the beginning of the yellow and brown walks. You have now more or less completed a circle. Your path soon rejoins the stream. Further along there is a circular water-collecting shaft in the stream, where the water joins a tunnel coming from Shing Mun Reservoir to the Plover Cove Reservoir for storage.

The path you are on joins the Forestry Road where you started the walk. Look out for a map provided by the Country Parks, on your left, of the Tai Po Kau Forest Reserve. You should be able to work out where you have been, and will find that you've made a combination of brown, yellow, red and blue walks.

Glossary

Achene A small, dry, one-seeded type of fruit which does not burst open when ripe. The fruit wall closely surrounds the seed, but is separate from it.

Acuminate Tapering to a slender point.

Acute apex The tip of any structure that is sharply pointed.

Adventitious root A root borne out of the ordinary sequence on roots, or on stems or leaves.

Alternate leaves Leaves arranged so that there is one leaf at each point of attachment to the stem, in more than one rank but not opposite, spiral or whorled.

Anther The part of a stamen that contains the pollen sacs.

Apex The tip.

Awn An elongate, bristle-like structure, especially found on the bracts (called *lemmas* or *glumes*) of grasses.

Axil The angle formed between the plant axis and any organ that arises from it, especially a leaf.

Axillary bud The bud that is always found in the leaf axil.

Axillary raceme A raceme that occurs in the axil of a leaf or bract.

Axis The main stem of a plant.

Basal Attached to the stem at ground level.

Berry A fruit that is fleshy throughout, having no hard layers. It may have one or many seeds.

Bipinnate Having the leaf blade *(lamina)* divided twice. Both primary and secondary divisions are pinnate.

Bract A modified leaf, especially one that subtends a flower or is associated with a flower.

Calyx The outer envelope of floral leaves, usually green.

Capitulum A flower-head made up of small flowers *(florets)*, as in the daisy and thistle of the Family Compositae.

Capsule   A dry fruit, developed from an ovary of several or many carpels, that opens in some way to shed the seed.

Carpel   The unit structure of an ovary, sometimes regarded as a floral leaf. One or more carpels may form the ovary.

Catkin   A type of inflorescence with numerous, unisexual flowers in the axils of scale-like bracts. The flowers often lack stalks and so form a type of spike, e.g. *Excoecaria agallocha*, the Milky Mangrove.

Caudate   Having a slender tail-like appendage.

Cauline   Arising from the stem, as in a cauline leaf as opposed to a basal leaf.

Column   A term applied particularly to members of the Orchid Family where the stamens, style and stigma are fused together to form one structure (column).

Compound leaf   Having the blade *(lamina)* divided into a number of separate segments (leaflets).

Corolla   A collective term for the petals of a flower; it usually refers to the brightly coloured inner whorl of the perianth.

Cotyledon   One of the first leaves formed on the embryo plant inside the seed, often called a *seed leaf*.

Crenate   Having rounded teeth along the leaf margin.

Cross pollination   The transference of pollen grains from the stamens of one flower to the stigma of another flower. The flowers must be on different plants for it to be true crossing, i.e. the uniting of different individuals in sexual reproduction.

Cyme   The type of inflorescence where the first flower to open is terminal, other flowers opening later below it. Such inflorescences are called cymose.

Deciduous   Having all leaves fall before the appearance of the new ones.

Dentate   Having teeth pointing outwards along the leaf margin.

Disc floret   The centrally placed tubular or bell-shaped florets of a capitulum, as in the yellow disc florets in the centre of a Daisy.

Distichous   Arranged in two diametrically opposite rows.

Drupe   A type of fruit that has a three-layered wall, the innermost layer being hard and woody forming the stone, e.g. the cherry or plum.

Ellipsoid   Elliptic in longitudinal section.

Elliptic   Oval with narrowed to rounded ends.

Entire   Having a leaf margin that is even, not toothed.

Ephemeral   Short-lived.

Epicalyx   A ring of bracts looking like sepals, but below the calyx, thus appearing to be a second calyx. It is characteristic of certain families, e.g. Malvaceae (Family of Hibiscus) and the Rosaceae (Family of the roses).

Epigynous   Having the sepals, petals and stamens on top of the ovary.

Epiphytes   Plants which grow physically on other plants but do not take food from them (i.e. ephiphytes are not parasites).

Filament   The stalk of an anther.
Filiform   Thread-like.
Flange   A projecting or outer rim of something, as on the corners of some square stems.
Floret   A small flower, usually in a dense group of such flowers.
Follicle   A type of fruit formed from a single carpel that is dry and splits open along one line to set the seed free, e.g. *Sterculia lanceolata* where five follicles are formed from each flower.
Frond   A leaf-like plant structure, as in Brown Seaweeds, but also commonly used in reference to fern leaves.

Glabrous   Without hairs; smooth.
Gland   A swelling containing secretory tissue. This term is sometimes used for swellings on leaves that are not actually secretory, e.g. Cassia leaves.
Glume   One of the lowest pairs of bracts in a grass spikelet.

Hirsute   Covered with long, distinct hairs.
Hispid   With rough hairs or bristles.
Hypogynous   Where the sepals, petals and stamens are borne below the ovary.

Inferior ovary   Where the ovary is below the point of expansion of the sepals, petals and stamens.
Inflorescence   The arrangement of flowers on the floral axis.
Internode   The portion of stem between two nodes.
Involucre   A ring of bracts surrounding a group of flowers as in the Compositae (Daisy Family).

Keel   A term commonly applied to the lowermost two petals in flowers of the Family Papilionaceae, e.g. Sweet Pea, where they are joined along one side to form a boat-like structure that encloses the stamens and the single carpel.

Labellum   The lowermost petal in an orchid flower that is usually much larger than the other two petals, often having three pronounced lobes.
Lamina   The flat expanded part of a leaf, also known as the blade.
Lanceolate   Lance-shaped.
Lateral   At the side.
Leaflet   The first division of a leaf lamina into separate segments; the term is often applied also to the second or third divisions of a leaf.
Leaf scar   The scar left on a stem when a leaf falls.

Ligule   The small scale-like flap in grasses found where the leaf blade joins the leaf sheath.

Linear   Narrow and several times longer than the width, as in the lamina of some leaves.

Lobe   A segment of a petal, calyx or leaf.

Nectary   A gland, commonly found in flowers, that stores or secretes a sugary fluid called nectar. It is much sought after by insects.

Node   The place on a stem where leaves are borne.

Nodule   A small, more or less spherical swelling.

Obtuse   Blunt or rounded at the end.

Once-pinnate   A leaf that is divided into a number of segments called leaflets; these are not further divided.

Ovary   The basal portion of a carpel. In some ovaries a number of carpels are joined to form the ovary. It surrounds and protects the female element in reproduction, the ovules.

Ovate   Shaped like a longitudinal section of a hen's egg.

Ovoid   A solid that is oval.

Ovule   The female element in réproduction. After fertilisation it becomes a seed.

Palmate   Having the lobes or the divisions of a structure arising from the same point. A palmate leaf has leaflets arranged in this way.

Palmately compound   Having a number of leaflets arising from the same point on a leaf, rather like the fingers of a hand.

Panicle   A complex type of inflorescence with many flowers that is basically a raceme, but is branched. Many grasses have a panicle inflorescence.

Papilla   A small, fleshy projection occurring anywhere on a plant.

Pappus   A crown of hairs, formed from the calyx, that serves as a parachute apparatus in wind dispersal of fruits, as seen in the Compositae (Daisy Family).

Pedicel   The stalk of a single flower.

Peduncle   The stalk of an inflorescence or partial inflorescence.

Pendulous   Hanging downwards.

Perennate   The ability of plants to survive from one winter to the next by various means.

Perennial   A plant that lives for more than two years, usually flowering each year.

Perianth   The floral leaves as a whole, including sepals and petals, if both are present. Particularly used when the calyx and corolla are not distinguishable, as in most Monocotyledons.

Perigynous   Having the sepals, petals and stamens borne around the ovary.

Persistent   Not falling off at maturity, as in leaves of evergreen trees.

Petal   A member of the inner series of perianth segments, if differing from the outer series, usually being brightly coloured.

Petaloid   Resembling a petal in colour and shape.

Petiole   The stalk of a leaf.

Photosynthesis   The process carried out by green plants in the presence of light where carbon dioxide and water are converted into simple sugars and oxygen is given off.

Pinnate   Composed of a number of leaflets arranged in two ranks along a common stalk.

Pinnatifid   Pinnately cut, but not into separate portions. The lobes are connected by lamina as well as midrib and stalk.

Placenta   The part of the ovary to which the ovules are attached.

Plumule   The young shoot of a seedling.

Pseudobulb   A thickened, bulb-like portion of the stem in some orchids.

Pulvinus   A swollen area, usually at the base of a leaf, that may be turgid (rigid) or flaccid. Change in turgor and hence shape may bring about movements of the leaf.

Raceme   An unbranched inflorescence, usually conical in outline, the growing points of which continue to add flowers to it so that there is no terminal flower. As the result of the mode of growth the oldest flowers are at the base of the floral axis and the youngest at the tip. Such inflorescences are called racemose.

Radicle   The young root of a seedling.

Ray florets   The outer strap-shaped flowers of a capitulum, as in the white ray florets of a Daisy.

Reticulate   Formed as a network.

Rhizome   An underground stem lasting more than one growing season.

Rhizomatous   Like a rhizome.

Scandent   Trailing.

Seed   A reproductive unit formed from a fertilised ovule.

Sepal   A member of the outer series of perianth segments, especially when green and more or less leaf-like.

Serrate   Having teeth like a saw.

Sessile   Without a stalk.

Spadix   A fleshy spike, usually with unisexual flowers and often associated with a spathe.

Spathe   A large ensheathing bract enclosing a spadix.

Spike   A simple racemose inflorescence with the flowers or spikelets lacking stalks.

Spikelet   The basic unit of a grass flowerhead, made up of two glumes and one or more florets.

Spur   A hollow, more or less conical, slender projection from the base of a perianth segment, often a petal. It may be part of the corolla.

Stamen   One of the male reproductive organs of a flowering plant.

Staminal tube   A tube formed from the fused filaments of the stamens as in Hibiscus and members of the Papilionaceae (Sweet Pea Family).

Standard petal   The large showy petal at the back of the flower in all members of the Papilionaceae (Sweet Pea Family).

Stellate   Star-shaped.

Stigma   The receptive surface of the female structure to which pollen grains adhere.

Stipules   The pair of scale-like or leaf-like appendages at the base of a petiole, sometimes joined to it.

Stolon   A creeping stem or runner, often formed by plants which have a central rosette of leaves or an erect stem. Stolons usually form roots at the nodes.

Style   The part of the female structure that connects the ovary with the stigma. It is often elongated and stalk-like.

Superior ovary   An ovary above the point of expansion of the sepals, petals and stamens.

Tap root   The main root derived directly from the radicle of a seedling.

Tendril   A climbing organ formed from the whole or part of a stem, leaf or petiole; it usually twines around supports. In Smilax the tendrils are formed from the stipules.

Terminal   At the end or apex.

Trifoliate   Three-leaved.

Tripinnate   Having the leaf blade divided three times, the first, second and third divisions being pinnate.

Umbel   An inflorescence in which all the flower stalks arise from the top of the main stem at the same point. In compound umbels the peduncles arise in the same way. The whole group of flowers is umbrella-shaped.

Valve   A section of a capsule after it has split open.

Whorled   Having organs that are arranged in a ring, the rings often encircling one another.

Suggested Reading

Allen, *Common Malaysian Fruits* (Longman, 1981).

Bentham, *Flora Hongkongensis* (Lovell Reeve, 1861).

Checklist of Hong Kong Plants (Agriculture and Fisheries Department Bulletin No. 1, 1978).

Chin, *Malaysian Flowers in Colour* (Tropical Press SDN, BHD, 1977).

Chin and Yoong, *Malaysian Fruits in Colour* (Tropical Press SDN, BHD, 1981).

Chong and Lee, *Chinese Medicinal Herbs of Hong Kong*, Vols. 1-2.

Clapham, Tutin and Warburg, *Flora of the British Isles* (Cambridge University Press, 1962).

Flora of Taiwan, 2nd ed., Vols. 1-6 (Epoch Publishing, 1980).

Dunn and Tutcher, *Flora of Kwangtung and Hong Kong (China)* (Royal Botanic Gardens, Kew, Bulletin of Miscellaneous Information (Additional Series 10), H.M. Stationery Office, 1912).

Edie, *Ferns of Hong Kong* (Hong Kong University Press, 1978).

Henderson, *Malayan Wild Flowers, Monocotyledons and Dicotyledons* (The Malayan Nature Society, reprinted 1974).

Herklots, *The Hong Kong Countryside* (South China Morning Post, 1965).

Hill, *Figs of Hong Kong*, (Hong Kong University Press, 1967).

Hill, Gott, Beth, and Hodgkiss, *Hong Kong Ecological Habitats, Flora and Fauna* (University of Hong Kong, 1978).

Hodgkiss, Thrower and Man, *An Introduction to the Ecology of Hong Kong*, 2 Vols. (Federal Publications (HK), 1981).

Illustrations of Higher Plants in China, Vols. 1-5 (Chinese Academy of Science).

Kuck and Tongg, *Hawaiian Flowers and Flowering Trees, A Guide to Tropical and Semitropical Flora* (Charles E. Tuttle Co., 1965).

Thrower, *The Order Leguminales* (University of Hong Kong, 1968).

Thrower, *Plants of Hong Kong* (Longman, 1971).

Tutcher, *Gardening for Hong Kong*, 4th ed. (South China Morning Post, 1964).

Urban Council Publications:
Hong Kong Food Plants (1981); *Hong Kong Freshwater Plants* (1978); *Hong Kong Orchids* (1980); *Hong Kong Poisonous Plants* (1981); *Hong Kong Shrubs* (1971); *Hong Kong Trees*, Vol. 1 (1972), Vol. 2 (1977).

Walden and Hu, *Wild Flowers of Hong Kong* (Sino-American Publishing Co., 1977).

Acknowledgements

The author and publisher wish to make grateful acknowledgement to Mr S.T. Chen, for much help in identifying specimens; Miss Merlyn Chesterman, for the drawing of all the pen and wash artwork within the text; Mr M.H. Ho, for the painting on the title page; and Dr W.J. Kyle, for the drawing of all the maps.

Index

Note: * colour photograph on this page

† illustrated on this page

Common Names

166

Turn-in-the-wind (*Mallotus paniculatus*) 48, 114

Twig-hanging Embelia (see also *Embelia laeta*) 107

Umbel-flowered Merremia (*Merremia umbellata*) 119

Walnut (*Juglans regia*) 30

Water Fern (*Azolla pinnata*) 21

Water Hyacinth (*Eichhornia crassipes*) 21, 99

Water Spinach (*Ipomoea aquatica*) 119

Wax Tree (see also *Rhus succedanea*) 57*, 104†

Waxy Leaf (see *Breynia fruticosa*)

Wedelia (*Wedelia chinensis*) 40, 110

Westland's Rhododendron (see also *Rhododendron westlandii*) 56*

White Bush Aster (*Aster baccharoides*) 27, 50, 120

White Mountain Aster (*Aster ageratoides*) 27, 28†

White Popinac (*Leucaena leucocephala*) 60, 64, 104

White Smartweed (*Polygonum lapathifolium*) 118

Wide-leaved St John's Lily (*Crinum latifolium*) 45

Wild Asparagus (*Asparagus cochinchinensis*) 110

Wild Cherry (*Prunus phaeosticta*) 131

Wild Citronella-grass (*Cymbopogon tortilis*) 27

Wild Coffee (*Psychotria rubra*) 26, 27, 32*, 40, 83, 95, 116

Wild Honeysuckle (*Lonicera japonica*) 64, 75, 76*

Wild Kudzu Vine (*Pueraria phaseoloides*) 60†

Wild Kumquat (see also *Fortunella hindsii*) 84†, 105

Wild Lettuce (see also *Lactuca indica*) 61

Wild Loquat (*Eriobotrya fragrans*) 53

Wild Mangosteen (*Garcinia oblongifolia*) 61, 111

Wild Mowtan Peony (*Melastoma candidum*) 26

Wild Mussaenda (*Mussaenda erosa*) 41

Wild Raspberry (*Rubus reflexus*) 41, 84, 115

Wild Violet (*Viola diffusa*) 55

Windy Hill Strobilanthes (*Strobilanthes apricus*) 31†

Wood-oil Tree (*Aleurites montana*) 64, 148

Woody Grass (*Imperata cylindrica*) 39, 42

Woolly Grass (*Philydrum lanuginosum*) 96†

Wright's Abacus Plant (*Glochidion wrightii*) 63

Yellow Basket-willow (*Engelhardtia chrysolepis*) 30

Yellow Camphor Tree (*Cinnamomum parthenoxylum*) 93

Yellow Poinciana (*Peltophorum pterocarpum*) 104†

Scientific Names

Abarema clypearia (Monkeypod) 123*, 130, 150

Abarema lucida (Chinese Apes-earring) 62, 130

Abelmoschus moschatus Medik (Musk Mallow) 44

Abutilon indicum (India Abutilon) 119

Acacia confusa 20, 24, 70, 114, 115, 121, 123*, 128

Inula cappa (Elecampane) 120, 128†
Ipomoea aquatica (Water Spinach) 119
Ipomoea braziliensis 21
Ipomoea digitata (Fingerleaf Morning Glory) 60, 136
Iris speculatrix (Hong Kong Iris) 57*, 63
Isachne globosa (Globose Twinball Grass) 96, 116, 117†
Ischaemum ciliare Retz (Indian Duckbeak) 96
Itea chinensis 64, 86
Ixeris 120
Ixeris sonchifolia 105

Juglans regia (Walnut) 30
Justicia procumbens (Purple Justicia) 115†

Kalanchoe flabellatum 42
Kandelia candel 38, 43, 80, 95, 98, 99, 100*

Lactuca indica (Wild Lettuce) 50, 61
Lactuca sativa (Lettuce) 51, 52†
Lantana camara 11, 73, 89
Lemmaphyllum microphyllum 148
Lepidosperma chinense (Chinese Scaly Seed) 140
Lepiota (Parasol Mushroom) 77*, 81
Leucaena leucocephala (White Popinac) 60, 64, 104
Ligustrum sinense (Chinese Privet) 49
Lilium brownii (Chinese Lily) 77*, 84
Limonium sinense (Sea Lavender) 43†
Lindernia cordifolia 118†
Liquidambar formosana (Sweet Gum Tree) 148, 151
Liriope spicata (Lily Turf) 42, 105†, 150
Litchi chinensis 20
Lithocarpus 20
Litsea cubeba (Fragrant Litsea) 127, 129, 149
Litsea glutinosa (Pond Spice) 48†, 129

Litsea rotundifolia (Round-leaved Litsea) 61, 63, 106, 129, 152
Lonicera japonica (Wild Honeysuckle) 64, 75, 76*
Lonicera macrantha (Large-flowered Honeysuckle) 52
Ludwigia 21
Ludwigia octovalis (Primrose Willow) 118, 122*
Lumnitzera racemosa 98, 100*
Lycopodium cernuum (Nodding Clubmoss) 28, 42
Lygodium japonicum (Climbing Fern) 63, 72, 148, 149
Lygodium microphyllum (Cav) R. Br. 148
Lygodium scandens Smartz 148

Macaranga tanarius (Elephant's Ear) 21, 92
Machilus breviflora (Short-flowered Machilus) 129
Machilus thunbergii (Red Machilus Tree) 62, 151, 152†, 154
Maclura cochinchinensis Lour. Corner (False Custard) 86
Maesa perlarius 37, 41, 86
Mallotus apelta 80
Mallotus paniculatus (Turn-in-the-wind) 48, 114
Manglietia fordiana 10
Melaleuca leucadendron (Paper-bark Tree) 126, 154
Melastoma candidum (Wild Mowtan Peony) 26, 27, 40, 83, 95
Melastoma dodecandrum (Creeping Melastoma) 28, 150
Melastoma sanguineum 40, 51, 61, 95, 96, 115, 131, 150-1, 153
Meliosma rigida (Stiff-leaved Meliosma) 153
Melodinus suaveolens (Mountain Orange) 57*, 67, 150, 154
Melothria heterophylla 83†

173

174

Strobilanthes apricus (Windy Hill Strobilanthes) 31†

Strychnos angustiflora 122*

Styrax odoratissimus (Fragrant Snow-bell) 66, 67†

Symplocos cochinchinensis (Retz.) Noot 153

Symplocos crassifolia 111

Symplocos decora Hance 54

Symplocos laurina (Retz.) Wall 153, 154

Symplocos panaliculata 84

Syzygium jambos (Rose-apple) 20, 148

Tetracera scandens (L) Merr. (Sand-paper Vine) 108, 120, 142, 150

Thysanolaena maxima (Tiger-grass) 128

Trentepohlia (Green Alga) 145*, 155

Tricalysia dubia 66†

Tristania conferta (see also Brisbane Box) 20, 70, 76*

Triumfetta bartramia 119

Turpinia arguta 111

Uraria macrostachya (Dog's Tail Bean) 84, 120

Utricularia (Bladderwort) 121

Uvaria microcarpa 33*, 37, 41

Vallisneria spiralis (Eel Grass) 21

Vernonia cinerea (Iron-weed) 74, 120, 138

Viburnum odoratissimum (Sweet Viburnum) 82

Viburnum sempervirens 40-1, 131

Viola diffusa (Wild Violet) 55

Vitex negundo (Negundo Chaste-tree) 86, 116†

Vitex rotundifolia 21, 81, 82†, 87

Wedelia chinensis (Wedelia) 118

Wedelia prostrata (Beach Wedelia) 21

Wickstroemia indica (Indian Wick-stroemia) 95, 142

Xanthium strumarium (Cocklebur) 87

Youngia japonica (Hawk's Beard) 54

Zanthoxylum avicennae (Prickly Ash) 64, 65, 114, 152, 154

Zoysia japonica (Korean Lawn Grass) 11

Zoysia sinica (Mangrove Grass) 42, 94